Bruised before Birth:
Parenting children exposed to
parental substance abuse

Acknowledgements

This book could not have even been started without support, information, an encouragement from many parents and professionals, or without financial assistanc from the US Children's Bureau. Despite many delays, this present form is ready t provide a springboard for further work.

Research for the technical information in this book was the accomplishment of Am Bullock, who, after completing a graduate degree in Public Administration, went o to work on a law degree focusing on child and family issues. What is presented i this book is data that was available to the public in 1993 and 1994. More will certainl emerge, and we may find that some of this new information will contradict or mak obsolete the preliminary work in the field.

The heart of the team effort in this book has been Liz Grimes. Liz and her husban Jac have been long-time advocates for children and are the parents of five childre all of whom came into their family after living with the effects of parental substanc abuse in some way. Liz contributed her perspective, insights, and practical knowledg to this project. She also encouraged her daughter Amanda to share with us as we giving further insights from a child's perspective. A special thank you to Amanc (and to her brothers Robbie and Zachary, and sisters Julie and Katherine).

As project director of a federal project on parent to parent supports in special nee foster care and adoption, my role has been to take information, insights, and practic suggestions, from our team and from other contributors, and try to put this all togeth into a form that could be used by families. As with any project, there is alway something more that could have been added, something left out, more we wish w could have done. This represents a start, and an encouragement for others to continu finding new information and ways to reach out to children exposed to parent substance abuse, and their families.

Joan McNamara
1994

Note to the UK edition

BAAF would like to express its sincere thanks to Joan McNamara for her ki permission to enable us to publish this UK edition. This edition essentially retai almost all of the original text; editorial changes have only been made whe terminology, legal references, and language use needed to be made more accessib to a UK readership.

Shaila Shah

Bruised before Birth

Parenting children exposed to parental substance abuse

UK EDITION

Joan McNamara

Amy Bullock and Elizabeth Grimes

for **B**_ritish_
A_gencies_
A_doption_
and **F**_ostering_

Published by
British Agencies for Adoption & Fostering
(BAAF)
Skyline House
200 Union Street
London SE1 0LY
Registered Charity 275689

© Family Resources, USA, 1994
© Joan McNamara and BAAF (UK edition) 1995

British Library Cataloguing in Publication Data
McNamara, Joan
  Bruised Before Birth: Parenting Children
  Exposed to Parental Substance Abuse
  I. Title
  362.7

  ISBN 1-873868-17-0

Designed by Andrew Haig & Associates
Typeset, printed and bound by Russell Press
(TU) in Great Britain

Contents

Introduction
A word to adoptive parents and foster carers

Because of increased awareness of the effect on children of drugs, alcohol, and other substances used by parents, especially by mothers during pregnancy, there is increased concern about what such influences will really mean for children and their families. Although there are many questions, it often seems that there aren't enough good answers: How many children will be exposed to parental substance abuse? Which children will be significantly or noticeably hurt? Will the effects be permanent? What will these be? How serious will these be? Can anything be done to change this? What will the children require medically, educationally, emotionally? What will parents and other adults need in order to help?

For foster carers and adoptive parents, these questions take on greater urgency. Many of the children in need of foster and adoptive homes come into care when adults are unable to parent appropriately due to problems such as substance abuse. In addition to the risks of prenatal exposure to substance abuse, children in families where there is drug and alcohol use are more likely to experience neglect, physical abuse and sexual abuse. Children with alcoholism in their family background may genetically be more at risk for vulnerability to alcoholism later on. The already challenging job of parenting becomes more complicated for families facing some of these issues.

One of the most important – and frustrating – words to keep in mind when struggling with these issues and questions is *maybe*. While there is no certainty in dealing with the possibilities and outcome for any child, there is even more uncertainty for these children at risk. We can only deal with probabilities, statistics, and information which may be outdated even before widely distributed. Prenatal exposure to drugs and alcohol is a serious and growing problem. But we cannot absolutely determine which children will be touched and in what ways. Not all children exposed prenatally to drugs and alcohol will automatically have severe problems. Attention has been focused in the media on the most dramatic aspects of the problem, using words like "crack baby" and "biological underclass". Responding to this, there has been some concern that there will be a flood of severely developmentally delayed children or those with multiple disabilities or learning difficulties in need of services as drug-exposed infants grow older. As drug testing for pregnant women and follow-up for drug-exposed children has become more widespread, however, the wide range of consequences has become more apparent: some children appear to have minimal or no apparent problems, others very significant problems, and many fall at various places in between.

Even though drugs like crack have had a great deal of publicity in terms of prenatal effects on children, it appears that prenatal use of alcohol (or alcohol in combination with other drugs) may have a more serious and long-term impact for children. Alcohol is said to be more powerful in its effect than any other drug, including cocaine. Alcohol may be the most commonly used drug, and the most readily available.

There also may be many more children not diagnosed formally as having Foetal Alcohol Syndrome or Effect (FAS or FAE) yet who still have educational and behavioural problems because of prenatal use of alcohol. It would be hard to measure the percentages of children affected by each type of substance, but if current thinking is correct, alcohol-affected children make up a large proportion of children who continue to have learning difficulties and other related issues beyond infancy. Since much of the long-term research and educational studies, as well as writing from parents, have focused on alcohol-affected children, and since many of the techniques and issues related to alcohol affected children are also relevant to children affected by other substances, this book has relied a great deal on this material.

There is no way to accurately predict what the specific needs will be for a particular child or how these will evolve. In fact, even when a maternal history of substance abuse is available (often it is not), pinpointing which problems are actually related to this and which are caused by other factors may be next to impossible. Not all health, education, and mental health professionals even know that substance abuse affects children in a variety of ways. Diagnosis can also be difficult:

some symptoms characteristic of Foetal Alcohol, for example, are very similar to or overlap with those due to other problems. Parents tell of times before a formal and accurate FAS or FAE diagnosis was finally given to their children, when various professionals diagnosed the problems and behaviours these children were displaying as due to Attachment Disorder, Attention Deficit Disorder, hyperactivity, autism, manic depressive disorder, oppositional defiant disorder, learning disabilities, emotional disturbance due to living with alcoholic parents, developmental delays, and poor parenting. This did not mean that their children could not have had some issues related to any of these labels, but that the primary diagnosis, the one most related to the factors causing these symptoms and the one which provided information that had the most success in developing appropriate home and educational plans, was FAS or FAE.

We still do not understand fully all of the factors that result in such different consequences for children. Current research studies in the USA are still exploring the complicated reasons and variables involved. In the meantime, families struggle to make sense of all this as they grapple with the daily realities of living with a child who may be affected by parental substance abuse.

Dr. Jerri Jenista is both a medical doctor and adoptive parent, with expertise in the medical issues that children may bring into foster and adoptive families. One of her excellent articles is included as a part of this book. She suggests that since there are so many unknowns, foster carers and adoptive parents, while striving to help children realise their highest potential, need to understand and be prepared for the possibility of significant problems. The motto *Hope for the Best, Prepare for the Worst* is particularly apt in this situation.

In addition to prenatal trauma from substance abuse, poor nutrition and lack of medical care during pregnancy, common with addicted mothers, can affect foetal health and development. Another complication is that the increased risks of developmental delays and emotional and behaviour problems can be exacerbated if a prenatally exposed child also lives within a drug influenced household. Parents who continue to abuse drugs and alcohol place their children at greater risk for abandonment, neglect, and abuse. Children growing up with substance abusing parents typically respond in a number of predictable ways: they may act up, withdraw, assume a parental role, pretend, deny feelings, and so on. But while some children appear, at least on the surface, to have adapted and manage to survive, others appear to react with exaggerated force to the emotional and physical chaos of a family struggling with addiction. Practical suggestions in this book from Liz Grimes, based on the wide-ranging needs of her own children and her advocacy and support work with other families, address some of the difficulties in parenting children exposed to parental substance abuse.

There is also a genetic impact for children: children with a family history of alcoholism, for example, are more likely to be vulnerable to alcoholism than children from non-alcoholic families. Without implying that the outcome is inevitable (which it isn't), children need to be helped to understand the "allergy" within their family of origin and be provided with information about alternatives and resources to cope with this genetic information. An article by Katherine Davis, social worker and adoptive parent, looks at some of the genetic issues, based on current theory and her own extensive research and experience.

There is no single profile that can describe all of the characteristics and needs of all children who may have been exposed to parental substance abuse. The potential problems are real but wide-ranging. The label "prenatal drug exposure" does not have to automatically mean a multi-problem, hopeless situation. The label "alcoholic family" does not have to automatically mean the pattern of addiction will be repeated in the next generation. But factors like these do present increased risks for a number of difficulties, both to the children and to the adults who care about them.

We know that children who grow up in the violence and poverty of inner cities, going home from overcrowded schools to stressed single parent families, are more likely to be caught up in cycles of violence and poverty around them. But this is not inevitable. After all, a child who grew up in such a situation became a candidate for President of the United States: Jesse Jackson, perhaps in part because of, instead of in spite of, his early experiences, grew into a strong, dynamic, and caring individual who touches the lives of others daily.

Each child is an individual with traits and talents shaped by an infinite variety of physical, genetic, and emotional influences. Even twins can have different physical, emotional, and biological reactions to life's challenges. If we were to make lists of typical characteristics under certain labels (boys are . . ., girls are . . ., two-year-olds are . . ., children with AIDS are . . ., children of alcoholics are . . ., and so on) for each orderly list there would be also be just as many variations, exceptions, and exaggerations . . . and that is good. Life would probably be predictable and static without this.

At the heart of a child's world, the family provides a safe place to trust and love, to grow and learn. But the family also provides the front line of protection, encouragement, and advocacy so important when a child has special needs. Foster and adoptive families often find that in addition to the usual roles of parents they must be archaeologists and architects for their children: uncovering, discovering or guessing about past influences and possible causes and then helping children repair, rebuild or compensate. Parents use a lot of common sense and sweat as they encourage their children to find their own unique talents and gifts in areas of creative intelligence that are not measured in academic tests. They may also be translators, interpreting the meanings of unfamiliar experiences, feelings, and behaviours to the child or to teachers or others about how these are different from the child's perspective.

Children hurt by life can begin to feel hopeless and helpless, victims of events beyond their control. They may view the world as a dangerous place full of undependable people and unexpected situations. They may not trust, or they may believe that there isn't any purpose in life, at least for them. We can view these feelings from a psychological perspective and talk of emotional problems. But in addition, we can also look at these negative beliefs as hurts to a child's spiritual development.

Whether one belongs to an organised faith community or even believes in God, there are usually important values in your life that make you feel a part of something larger than yourself, and that there are things worth fighting for: it might be helping others as part of a formal religious creed or it might be feeling part of the universe and working to save the environment. Whatever it is, it often can make you feel more positive and optimistic about yourself and about life. Numerous studies have pointed to the benefits of believing positively in something beyond yourself in the challenge of recovering from emotional or physical hurt. Some families have found that helping a child develop a sense of relationships and empathy within a set of positive values and beliefs, and putting those into action altruistically, can help a child in developing skills as a survivor instead of as a victim. A child who has a sense of optimism about the future, who has learned to feel capable and lovable, usually has a stronger foundation to face challenges.

Parenting a child who has or may develop some special needs means more complications in the difficult challenge of parenting. It can mean more work, more stress, and more time. There can be hours spent seeking services and convincing these to help, attending programmes, and working with the child, hours of frustration, encouragement, sadness, joy, and prayer. Besides information and concrete services, most of all parents need connection with others who understand first hand what it means to love and parent a child with special needs; they need time out to be adults sharing, and time away from their children.

The most important help to families will not necessarily be professionals and programmes, but other parents. Only other parents and carers will truly understand from the heart both the pain and the positives of helping a beloved child who marches with a different rhythm. It will be another parent who will understand that sharing a long litany of complaints and frustrations means you need to vent feelings, not disrupt a placement. If you are fortunate enough to belong to a parent support group, or have families you can call on for emotional and practical support, your family has been given a valuable gift.

Diagnostic services, educational and vocational programmes, parent support groups, mental health services, medical services, and many other resources can be helpful for some children affected by parental substance abuse and their families, but often these are not accessible or not experienced with substance abuse issues. Yet day by day, the knowledge base and services and supports are expanding. We hope that throughout this book we have been able to balance realistic information currently available (which may be outdated tomorrow) with a sense of optimism about the future for children and their families.

1   Bruised before birth

The report on the social worker's desk profiles a child with a long list of problems at school and at home. These include difficulties following directions, paying attention, and moving from one task to another, in addition to becoming easily frustrated, and obvious lying. It describes the child's difficulty in giving or receiving affection and difficulty with eye contact yet inappropriate touching of other children, and the child's difficulty respecting other people's space and property. This child is called friendly, charming, and bright, but seems to make the same mistakes and misbehaviours over and over again. This child appears verbal, but doesn't always articulate clearly or understand or act on what is being said. In addition to having trouble making and keeping friends at school, there are also learning problems. If a label were given to the child in this report, which would be more likely?

a) Attention Deficit Disorder, with or without hyperactivity
b) Emotional problems from growing up in a neglectful or substance-abusing family.
c) Post-Traumatic Stress Disorder from early experiences of physical and/or sexual abuse
d) Attachment Disorder
e) Foetal Alcohol Effect, Foetal Alcohol Syndrome, or other issues related to prenatal substance abuse
f) None of the above
g) A mixture of the above

The problem with these labels is that so many of the behaviours or symptoms described in the report could cover more than one diagnostic description. Indeed, some children will have more than one reason for behaviours. A child who is born to an alcoholic mother and lives in this family for several years, where he or she is also sexually abused, may have several interrelated problems: prenatal alcohol exposure may have meant a cranky, hypersensitive baby difficult to nurture which, when combined with a possibly neglectful alcoholic mother, could contribute to attachment difficulties; lack of structure and early neglect can compound difficulties of learning differences; the child's emotional and environmental vulnerabilities make physical and sexual abuse an increased possibility, with resulting emotional problems. Which of these circumstances is the cause of any one problem the child has? Which problems caused by one factor are aggravated or made worse by other problems? And if we cannot make at least some educated guesses about the causes for behaviours, how will we be able to find the most effective ways to help this child and other similar children?

One of the main reasons to use a diagnostic label when working with a child is to figure out the *why* (or, more often, whys) so that you can more accurately and effectively plan *what* to do and *when* to help this child. We cannot always know the reasons why something went wrong, but for any individual child if we look at all of the clusters of signs and symptoms, behaviours and characteristics, we may be able to see a pattern similar to others. It won't be identical, since each child is unique, but there may be a number of points of connection.

With children coming from substance abusing families into foster care and adoption, often several different patterns, reflecting physical, genetic, and emotional experiences, overlap to make that child's particular mosaic. Some parts may not be available for us to look at, like prenatal history, or descriptions of abuse. Parents and professionals then have to do detective work to make assumptions about these to add to the picture. Tracking down and developing appropriate structures and services that can help children make the most of their potential requires stubbornness, flexibility and creativity. That may also be a description of what is required when parenting children exposed to parental substance abuse.

In the end, what substance a birth parent may have ingested may not be as important as what symptoms you can see in the child in front of you. Many times parents have had to work backwards, so to speak: there was no prenatal history available, but certain patterns of symptoms and behaviours are obvious and others are possible. From these outward signs the parents have to work out, with the help of professionals, what the causes might be and what the responses should be. Like an archaeologist, detective, or a parent trying to understand the cryptic directions for a complicated toy, sometimes that little piece that doesn't fit doesn't matter in the end; it's the whole picture that is important.

Children who are hyperactive because of emotional problems which may be responsive to therapeutic interventions may not benefit from medication for hyperactivity prescribed for a child with Attention Deficit Disorder. A child who has difficulties with cause and effect thinking because of prenatal substance abuse probably would not get full benefit from a behaviour modification programme designed for another child with delayed development. At the same time, a child with learning disabilities who has also experienced abuse may need adaptations in both therapy and school situations because of the complex interaction of these two stressors in his or her life. Just as each child is different, the mix of resources and responses for each child will need to be different. This can be an enormous balancing act for parents, who are primary advocates for their children.

The earlier the diagnosis of what this pattern of issues is for a child, and the earlier appropriate intervention can be put into place, the better the opportunities for successfully reaching full potential. A nurturing, stable family which can provide both a secure, consistent structure and yet be flexible enough to creatively respond to this child's particular needs is the best foundation. It is also a tall order. When the school can provide the same kind of positive environment, focusing on and building on what the child *can do*, not what the child cannot, then the foundation for learning and growing becomes even more grounded. As parents, we have to work to make sure that both family and school are working together to recognise and meet the child's needs, and to celebrate his or her strengths.

NOTE: The charts, lists, and suggestions in this book reflect just *some* of the possibilities and realities for children and their families. Not all children who may have been affected by parental substance abuse will demonstrate any or all of the traits listed.

2 How substances used by mothers can affect unborn children

There are many substances we know of which can hurt children still growing inside their mothers: legal substances like tobacco and alcohol and prescription drugs; illegal substances like street drugs. Most drugs can have a negative effect on a developing foetus, with the potential for problems after birth. Poor nutrition, especially in combination with use of any of these substances and without regular prenatal care, can also have a profound negative influence.

Most substances hurt an unborn child through damaging the developing organs or brain. Although some of this damage results in temporary effects after birth and in infancy, others are more long-lasting or permanent. For example, some newborns and infants may have types of respiratory problems or chronic irritability which may not be major influences on later development. Some children may be born with symptoms that are remediable, such as certain heart defects and cleft palate, and still other children may have problems that present life-long challenges, such as learning differences, cerebral palsy, or mental retardation.

There is no scientific equation measuring how much and how often a pregnant woman can use or abuse a particular substance to determine if and in what way and how much her child will be affected. There have been situations where one twin was affected seriously by prenatal substance abuse and the other was not. We do know that use of certain substances during pregnancy significantly increases the number and severity of birth defects and long-term problems for children, and that these effects or characteristics tend to cluster in certain patterns. Medically speaking, a cluster of symptoms or signs that indicates a particular condition is often referred to as a syndrome.

The most commonly studied, and perhaps the most common, of these clustered symptoms is related to the effects of alcohol. Children born to mothers who abuse alcohol often have a similar grouping of physical, behavioural, and intellectual traits. The most obvious form of this cluster is referred to as Foetal Alcohol Syndrome (FAS), and the form with fewer identified symptoms is referred to as Foetal Alcohol Effect (FAE).

Alcohol

In 1973, Jones and Smith were among the first to research a pattern of abnormalities among children born to alcoholic women. These researchers labelled the abnormalities "Foetal Alcohol Syndrome" (FAS).[1] Foetal Alcohol Syndrome is now the leading cause of severe learning disability in the USA. It is also the one type of learning disability which is totally preventable. Not every child affected by prenatal alcohol exposure will experience severe learning disability, but learning disabilities are common and significant effects.

Although statistics vary widely with regards to the numbers of children born each year who are alcohol affected, the most widely accepted statistics indicate that around 40,000 children affected by alcohol are born every year in the USA. One of the most discouraging aspects about alcohol is that a woman can actually harm the foetus before she even realises she is pregnant. Because no safe level of drinking during pregnancy has been established, it is recommended that mothers abstain from drinking altogether during pregnancy. Breast-feeding is also to be discouraged among nursing mothers who consume alcohol.

The primary, and often most obvious, damage that alcohol exposure causes is to the central nervous system. This damage to the brain can range from mild to severe, and interferes with learning. Developmental delays are common for alcohol-affected children, but even for children only mildly affected this can interfere with the ability to relate one piece of information to another. Think of the brain like a computer and imagine what would happen if someone spilled beer on the keyboard. Even if just a little of the alcohol damaged the circuitry, there would still be some malfunctions: the computer might function well sometimes and not others; there might be difficulties storing or retrieving information; difficulties processing data; or a slower speed to get to the correct data. These problems are similar for alcohol-affected children, whether they are tested as being below or above average in intelligence.

Again, it is important to emphasise that little is known about factors determining whether a child will develop alcohol-related problems, or how significant these will be. There is no cut off point that indicates that a specific amount of alcohol at a specific time will create certain types of problems, and less than this will not. It has been proposed, however, that mothers who maintain adequate nutrition even though drinking may give birth to children less severely affected than mothers who have poor nutrition.

Foetal Alcohol Syndrome
Foetal Alcohol Syndrome (FAS) is a term used to describe a pattern of physical, behavioural, and intellectual characteristics children may display when prenatally exposed to alcohol. These developmental effects are permanent and not correctable, but most children can still benefit and grow within families and make progress to prepare for adulthood. There is a wide range of intellectual functioning for individuals diagnosed as having FAS, from having severe learning disabilities to above average functioning, although a large proportion fall into the first range. Most people with FAS have some type of difficulty with information processing.

In order to obtain a medical diagnosis of FAS a cluster of symptoms must be present in the child. Within each of three categories that typify FAS a child must have at least one characteristic. The three categories of symptoms include:

1. Growth deficiency for height and weight: before and/or after birth the child is smaller, grows more slowly than the norm; sometimes referred to as growth retardation.
2. A distinct pattern of facial features and physical characteristics: children born with FAS may have a flat midface, short upturned nose, thin upper lip, and smaller eye folds, for example. It is often the distinct facial characteristics that confirm a diagnosis.
3. Central nervous system dysfunction: characteristics that point to damage to the central nervous system may be severe, such as learning difficulties and small head, or more subtle, such as learning disability and poor co-ordination. Symptoms such as hyperactivity, which is very common, and poor co-ordination are also possibilities that could add up to a diagnosis of FAS. Behavioural traits like these are common to many children, so it makes determination more difficult.

FAS is not determined by just one symptom, or just one set of symptoms.

Known maternal history of drinking during pregnancy provides more impetus to look at FAS as a possible cause or contributor to problems and potential problems. Because a child has FAS does not mean that he or she could not also have other medical, physical, or emotional problems, related to or distinct from their FAS diagnosis. All problems a child may be presenting do not automatically have to be related to alcohol effects. Even the facial features used as an important diagnostic marker may not be sufficient to determine FAS unless you compare the child to other relatives. Lowset ears or small eyes could actually be family traits, characteristics that run in that family.

Intrauterine growth retardation is a phrase used to describe a slower growth rate than normal for a child during the pregnancy. This may be used to describe some children with FAS, particularly if full term children are born at a much lower birth weight and height. Children with FAS may remain short and skinny for their age although some girls may gain weight during puberty and may even become slightly overweight.

The distinct facial characteristics present right from birth for some children with FAS can alert professionals to a possibility of this diagnosis. Facial anomalies of FAS children can include small wide-set eyes, a smooth philtrum (no groove between lip and nose), flat midface, simply formed and/or lowset ears, a thin upper lip, short upturned nose, a small head circumference, and epicanthric folds (folds at the corner of the eyes). Other facial characteristics that may be seen include a receding chin, crossed eyes, short eye slits, and dental abnormalities.

Children with FAS may experience a wide range of other physical problems including heart defects, urogenital problems, hearing difficulties, hydrocephaly, and curvature of the fingers. Unlike narcotic drugs, alcohol can attack practically any of the body's cells, and this may be the reason for the facial and other physical characteristics.

Prenatal alcohol exposure also contributes to central nervous system dysfunction which, to oversimplify, means that the main human computer that controls the body doesn't operate as it should. This can manifest itself in a variety of ways, such as hypersensitivity to touch, light, or sound; hyperactivity and distractibility; and difficulty in processing verbal information properly.

Whether their intellectual abilities are measured as below average,

Table 1

Some physical effects of Foetal Alcohol Syndrome (FAS) that are seen in children

Facial abnormalities	*Other problems*
no groove between lip and nose	heart defects
upturned, short nose	underweight
thin upper lip	cerebral palsy
receding chin	hydrocephaly
cleft lip and palate	epilepsy
poor eyesight	dental abnormalities
short eye slits	hearing difficulties
small wide set eyes	urogenital problems
drooping eyelids	club foot
crossed eyes	stiff joints
	curvature of the fingers

borderline, normal, or above average, many children with FAS have great difficulty with skills such as cause and effect thinking, generalising information, and telling time. Adolescents can still have problems with abstract reasoning skills, impulsiveness, and making age-appropriate judgements. This puts them at increased risk for being victimised emotionally, financially or sexually. One father described his son in relation to these problems: "He's a smart enough kid, but he doesn't have enough common sense." Uneven performance and uneven memory skills make it harder for children and adults with FAS to use the skills and intellectual strengths they do have.

Foetal Alcohol Effects (FAE)

Foetal alcohol effects (FAE) are far more widespread within the general population than FAS. Although FAE has often been described as a less severe form of FAS it is more accurate to describe it as the form of alcohol related insult to development that has fewer or less apparent symptoms, particularly physical characteristics. This makes it harder to diagnose. According to Michael Dorris in his book, *The Broken Cord*,[2] in many ways

FAE can be just as debilitating as the full syndrome. Children with FAE fall within a similar range of intellectual functioning as with FAS, but are more likely to test in the average to above range than children with FAS.

Children with FAE, whether diagnosed or undiagnosed, may look "normal" and have average intelligence, yet still have similar difficulties with information processing and other problems associated with FAS. They may be challenged by learning differences but, as with other forms of learning disabilities, may struggle with an "invisible" disability. This makes it more difficult for others to recognise and accept their need for assistance. Ironically, the higher the level of intellectual functioning, and the more "normal" the child appears, the less likely is the child to get needed services.

The adults around them, from parents to teachers to neighbours, even professionals, may assume that because this child looks, talks and tests within normal range, she or he should be expected to act that way. They feel that children who look "normal", and who do not have a learning disability, should be able to act like other children. Adults unfamiliar with the child's special needs may assume that a child is being stubborn, or lazy, or wilfully disobedient. Instead, the child is often having difficulty dealing with the flood of stimuli in the environment and difficulty sorting out what is expected in their situation. Children who have learning difficulties because of alcohol exposure can't always act like other children. They may be hyperactive, more easily stressed, and have difficulty processing directions and commands accurately. This leads to conflicts with adults and to lowered self-esteem. Diane Malbin[3] points to research indicating that children with FAE who have average and above average IQ scores often have the most difficulty adjusting to the world around them. Without specific strategies, environmental accommodations, and training on how to cope in the larger world, alcohol affected children, as some professionals describe it, are struggling, rather like a person trying to get around Liverpool with a road map of Leeds.

FAS/FAE: Challenges and possibilities
In a very brief period of time the effects of prenatal exposure to alcohol have been recognised, despaired of, examined, and re-evaluated. We now know that early studies[4,5,6,7] done on children growing up without diagnosis, stability, intervention, or hope, provided us with one measure for alcohol-

affected children: the far end of the scale, where despair is commonplace. We now also know that there are studies[8,9,10,11,12] and examples which provide other measures: children who, within their own widely ranging patterns of limits and strengths, can benefit from individualised strategies, consistent structure, and the love of families of their own.

We still have a long way to go, however, in community understanding of prenatal substance abuse in general, and the needs of children in particular. Even professionals may not be familiar with the learning differences and processing problems that alcohol affected children can have. Children may be punished for oppositional behaviour when they are actually frustrated by an overload of information and stimuli.

Old information and stereotypes about children with learning disabilities, and FAS/FAE in particular, may present barriers for children. For example, it was assumed that alcohol-affected children had limited conscience. In part this was based on observations of children who seemed to have no hesitation in stealing or lying, and repeated the behaviours seemingly without remorse. Recently, however, it has been pointed out that for children who have difficulty with memory and with information processing, lying can often be an attempt to present an answer, any answer, instead of a deliberate attempt to deceive. Stealing can also be due to various reasons if one considers the motivations of those children who do not have an understanding of object relationship and boundaries, of children reacting to stress with impulsivity rather than cause and effect, and of developmentally delayed children who may still be at self-centred levels of development like that of toddlers. Children with FAS/FAE who have been given opportunities to bond to dependable adults can demonstrate empathy and loyalty to friends and family and empathy towards others.

It has been suggested that although there is a cluster of predominantly negative symptoms associated with alcohol affected children it is possible that there may also be (or could be encouraged) a cluster of more positive characteristics. Older research studies and the media often portray individuals with FAS or FAE with a sense of hopelessness, describing problems like isolation, depression, aggression, and social immaturity. But as newer research and, especially, the perspective of parents and professionals working proactively with alcohol-affected children and adults has been considered, different images are emerging. With

Table 2

Some signs that may indicate prenatal exposure to alcohol

Infancy	Early childhood	Childhood	Adolescence
eating difficulties	eating problems	learning disabilities	problems with abstract thinking
sleeping problems	sleeping difficulties	poor socialisation skills	maths difficulties
central nervous system dysfunction	body rocking	problems making and keeping friends	social withdrawal
failure to thrive	clumsiness	poor co-ordination	difficulty keeping jobs
growth retardation	underweight and skinny	poor cause and effect thinking	impulsiveness
small head circumference	short memory span	uneven memory	problems with recognising boundaries
attachment difficulties	brief attention span	easily distractible	often at increased risk for victimisation

supportive intervention and individualised strategies for coping with life's challenges, many more alcohol-affected individuals have been able to develop constructive lifestyles. More accurate diagnostic recognition of FAS/FAE makes it clear that individuals with these labels have been struggling and succeeding in our communities, as business people, constructions workers, cooks, teachers, parents, medical technicians, and a host of other occupations. These adults and their families will often share how difficult it was, and still is, to find ways to deal with gaps and uneven skills. But they can also share their success in leading positive and independent lives. Not all children with FAS or FAE will have

17

minimal intellectual functioning or poor social abilities.

Parents point out that children who may have trouble with information processing may instead display creativity in music, art, cooking, gardening, individual sports, and caring for the world around them. Despite stereotypes about lack of conscience and about aggressive behaviour, many securely bonded alcohol-affected children are loyal to family, friends and pets, are socially engaging, and may have increased sensitivity to others and their feelings. It is upto parents and others who care about these children to provide them with the emotional and practical encouragement to find and develop these talents.

Parents and professionals share stories about children who have a deep, fiercely held sense of justice and can be counted on to reach out to those who may be mistreated, scapegoated, or excluded. If these children look at the world from a different perspective, this may mean they perceive things in far from ordinary ways.

Marijuana
Although marijuana is a relatively old drug and commonly used, the effects of marijuana use during pregnancy still remain unclear. The inconsistencies of marijuana research may be explained partly due to the fact that it is difficult to separate the effects of marijuana from other factors such as the mother's health and parenting skills. Another reason for the unclear findings regarding the effects of marijuana stems from the fact that these are hard to separate from the effects of other drugs. Marijuana is often used in conjunction with other drugs such as alcohol, cigarettes, and cocaine. It is difficult to isolate the effects of one drug when polydrug use is so common.

Research has indicated that tetrahydrocannabinol (THC), the chemical in marijuana that produces a "high", can easily cross the placental barrier. When this chemical crosses the placental barrier it reduces the amount of oxygen present within the foetal blood. Unlike many other drugs, research on marijuana use has shown that this substance probably does not increase the risk of miscarriages and still births.[13,14]

Several studies, however, do indicate that marijuana may adversely affect the sleeping patterns and visual functioning of children.[15] Research has shown that marijuana use during pregnancy can adversely impact on the sleep and arousal patterns of newborns, although the long-term outcomes of this finding are unknown.[16] One recent study concluded that children who were prenatally exposed to marijuana were slower in visual responsiveness than children who were not exposed.[17,18,19]

It is possible that when marijuana is combined with other substances it may increase the effects. Marijuana use during pregnancy when combined with poor prenatal care and the use of alcohol and other drugs can greatly increase the risk of negative consequences for the unborn child. The effects of marijuana are summarised below.

Table 3

Possible effects of marijuana

Infancy	*Childhood*
premature birth	sleep problems
low birth weight	learning problems
shaking and trembling	visual problems
may startle easily	other unknowns
sleep problems	

Sources:
Harrison D, "Drug Exposed Infants", *Growing Together* 4 (8):1, 1989, USA
American Council for Drug Education, *Drugs and Pregnancy: It's not worth the risk*, 1991, USA

Heroin

Heroin is an opium derivative that is frequently used in the USA and increasingly in the UK. Heroin can be snorted or smoked but it is usually injected into a vein under the skin. Heroin addicts are commonly treated with methadone, a synthetic narcotic, to help ease the effects of withdrawal. Although children can be born addicted to both heroin and/or methadone, babies born to mothers receiving methadone under medical supervision tend to have fewer complications than babies born to heroin addicts or methadone users who are not receiving medical care and adequate nutrition.

Heroin use by pregnant women has been strongly linked to increases in the risks of stillbirths, neonatal deaths and foetal distress. Heroin use is also related to an increased risk of Sudden Infant Death Syndrome (SIDS).

Due to the fact that heroin is usually injected directly into the vein, there is also an increased risk of HIV infection. According to the Center for Disease Control (CDC), over half of the women with AIDS in the USA obtained the disease through intravenous (IV) drug use. This intravenous drug use has been linked to four out of every five cases of paediatric AIDS in the USA.

Heroin use is also strongly linked to pregnancy complications such as abruptio placentae, breech presentations, premature labour and Caesarian sections. Heroin addicted mothers often deliver early and their premature babies may experience brain haemorrhages and foetal respiratory distress syndrome. Although heroin use is usually not associated with physical malformations, it has been linked to strabismus, a common visual disorder in which the eyes do not focus properly.

Infants born to mothers who used heroin during pregnancy often experience withdrawal symptoms shortly after birth, such as tremors, poor feeding and sleeping patterns, vomiting, and diarrhoea. These infants may be irritable for several months. Parents need to handle these infants with care and take precautions against over-stimulating the baby.

Table 4

Signs that may indicate prenatal exposure to heroin

Infancy	*Childhood*
withdrawal	short attention span
irritability	mood swings
feeding problems	vision problems
sleeping problems	hearing problems
increased risk for SIDS	hyperactivity, hypersensitivity
increased risk for AIDS	learning disabilities
may be small in size	speech difficulties

Sources:
Harrison D, "Drug Exposed Infants", *Growing Together* 4 (8):1, 1989, USA
American Council for Drug Education, *Drugs and Pregnancy: It's not worth the risk*, 1991, USA

The long-term effects of heroin and methadone exposure are somewhat difficult to determine. Some children born prenatally exposed to heroin may have hyperactivity, short attention spans, and visual problems but normal intellectual and physical development. Others may have more serious problems.

Cocaine

Cocaine, an extract of the coca plant, is a powerful drug that can easily result in physical and psychological addiction. Cocaine may be sniffed, smoked, or injected under the skin. Crack is the street name for a form of freebase cocaine that has been manufactured into crystals or "rocks"; when smoked through a pipe these rocks will produce a cracking noise. Crack cocaine is considered to be more powerful than powdered cocaine. Cocaine is frequently used in combination with other drugs. For example, speedballing, which involves injecting a heroin and cocaine mixture directly under the skin, is a fairly popular technique among addicts in some countries.

Cocaine and crack cocaine have received a lot of publicity related to birth defects and prenatal damage. The term "crack baby" came into the vocabulary through media coverage about pregnant mothers who were also addicts. However, long-term studies seem to indicate that although consequences can be serious for unborn children, cocaine use alone may have fewer and less serious effects than chronic alcohol use during pregnancy. This is not to minimise the very real negative effects cocaine can have, but to place it in perspective in the list of negative influences on pregnancy.

Cocaine use is associated with pregnancy complications, including an increased risk for miscarriages, abruptio placentae, and early delivery. Even if the infants are not born prematurely, cocaine use during pregnancy is linked to a lowered birthweight, shorter length, and smaller head circumference. Mothers who stop using cocaine during pregnancy, even in the last trimester, are more likely to improve intrauterine growth as compared to babies who were exposed to cocaine throughout the entire pregnancy. However, cocaine use during the first trimester can cause irreversible damage to the placental and uterine blood vessels.

As stated earlier, cocaine use is strongly associated with intrauterine growth retardation. This may be related to the fact that cocaine often suppresses the appetite of the user, thereby resulting in poor nutrition. Cocaine exposed infants do not experience as intense a drug withdrawal as do children exposed to heroin. However, these babies are often jittery, easily startled, and irritable. These infants may cry a lot and be extremely sensitive to their surroundings. They may have difficulty falling asleep and may be easily awakened once they are asleep. These behaviours are thought to be direct effects of cocaine.

Cocaine exposure is also associated with neurological complications. Infants tend to have unusually stiff muscles and toddlers also have difficulty with muscle control. In addition, defects in the genitalia and urinary tract have also been observed among cocaine exposed infants.

As with heroin use, injecting cocaine increases the risk of infection from the human immunodeficiency virus (HIV) that causes AIDS. Infants prenatally exposed to cocaine are also at an increased risk of contracting sexually transmitted diseases from the mother.

Few research results are available regarding the later effects of prenatal cocaine exposure as experienced by older children and adolescents. Some research has indicated that compared to other children, three to five-year-olds who had been exposed to cocaine prenatally tended to be more hyperactive, extremely sensitive to their environment, and either withdrawn or aggressive in the classroom.[18,19] But other studies have not found such clear-cut differences, except for hyperactivity.[20,21,22,23,24] One of the problems in research has been that so many of the mothers studied also used alcohol and/or tobacco, perhaps in addition to other illegal drugs. As we keep repeating, it is very difficult to discriminate between the effects of the various substances, and the effects of other circumstances, such as poor nutrition and poor maternal health.

Testing newborns for drug exposure
Based on an interview by Liz Grimes with Dr Jerri Jenista, MD, 10 December 1992

Newborns can be tested for prenatal drug exposure by testing the first stool after birth (meconium) for the suspected drugs. During the first week of life, a hair analysis can be used to reveal drug exposure. According to testing done at the University of Michigan in Detroit,

Table 5

Signs that may indicate prenatal cocaine exposure

Infancy	Early childhood	Older childhood
withdrawal symptoms	may be unco-	motor skills
sleep difficulties	ordinated	difficulties
startles easily	speech difficulties	learning difficulties
a high pitched cry	mood swings	easily frustrated
very stiff posture	tantrums	tantrums
irritability	poor impulse control	poor impulse control
hypersensitivity	irritability	difficulty with stress
avoidance of eye	hypersensitivity	hyperactivity
contact	attachment difficulties	attachment problems
growth retardation	may be small in size	mood swings
feeding problems	poor feeding skills	poor judgement
visual abnormalities	vision problems	vision problems
small head	easily distracted	short spans of
circumference		attention

approximately 40 per cent of drug exposed infants are misdiagnosed when only urine and/or maternal history are used as diagnostic tools.

Drug screens will usually test for the common drugs of abuse. If you request that drug screening be done for a newborn, you may want to be specific in requesting which drugs to test for, particularly if the birth mother's history indicates certain substances. If you suspect a particular one, you need to specifically request that it be included in the testing procedures with the proper consent of the parent.

Remember, just because a birth mother says she did not use cocaine, for example, or the drug test indicates no cocaine, does not mean that other substances were not used during pregnancy. There could be a number of street drugs the birth mother did use during pregnancy, some of which may not have been included in the routine drug testing. If the birth mother has been using what is called a "designer drug", for example, Ecstasy, chances are that this will not be included in the common drug screen.

If possible, the birth mother needs to be asked directly about what she used during pregnancy, even substances used "just once" or in the period directly before she realised that she was pregnant. Again, if you know about a specific substance, or suspect it, request a drug screen for that substance.

Unfortunately, there are no testing procedures or screens that will accurately determine prenatal alcohol exposure. This is where a thorough social and medical history of both birth parents can be extremely important.

References

1 Jones K L, and D W Smith, 'Recognition of Foetal Alcohol Syndrome in Infancy', *Lancet* 2: 999-10001, 1973.

2 Dorris M, *The Broken Cord*, New York, Harper Perennial, 1989, USA.

3 Malbin D, *Fetal Alcohol Syndrome and Fetal Alcohol Effect: Strategies for professionals*, Minnesota, Hazeldon 1993, USA.

4 Streissguth A P, *A Manual of Adolescence and Adults with Fetal Alcohol Syndrome with Special References to American Indians*, Seattle, Washington, Departmental of Psychiatry and Behavioural Sciences, and the United States Department of Health and Human Services, 1988, USA.

5 Streissguth A P, 'Psychological and Behavioural Effects in Children Prenatally Exposed to Alcohol', *Alcohol, Health, and Research World*, Rockville, Maryland, National Clearing House for Alcohol Information, 1985, USA.

6 Abel E L, *Alcohol Syndrome and Fetal Alcohol Effects*, New York, Plenum Press, 1984, 1987, USA.

7 Abel E L, and Sokel R J, 'Incidents of Fetal Alcohol Syndrome and Economic Impact of FAS-Related Anomalities' *Drug and Alcohol Dependence* 19:51-70, 1987, USA.

8 Chasnoff I J, *Guidelines for Adopting Drug-Exposed Infants and Children*, Chicago Illinois, National Association for Perinatal Addiction Research and Education, 1992, USA.

9 Barth R P, and Needell B, *Outcomes for Drug-Exposed Children Four Years Post Adoption*, Berkely, California, Family Welfare Research Group, School of Social Welfare, 1994, USA.

10 Barth R P, 'Adoption of Drug-Exposed Children: Development outcomes and parental satisfaction' *Children and Youth Services Review* 13 (1991): 323-342, USA.

11 Kleinfeld J and Wescott S, eds, *Fantastic Antoine Succeeds: Experiences in educating children with Fetal Alcohol Syndrome*, Fairbanks, Alaska, University of Alaska Press, 1993, USA.

12 Englemann J, *A Woman's Loss of Choice, A Child's Future: How alcohol and other drug use during pregnancy affect our children*, Center City, Minnesota, Hazelden, 1993, USA.

13 Fried P A, and O'Connell CM, 'Comparison of the Effects of Prenatal Exposure to Tobacco, Alcohol, Cannabis, and Caffeine on Birth Size and Subsequent Growth', *Neurotoxicology and Teratology* 9(2): 79-85, 1987, USA.

14 Zuckerman B, Frank D A, Hingson R, et al, 'Effects of Maternal Marijuana and Cocaine use on Fetal Growth', *New England Journal of Medicine*, 320: 762-768, 1989, USA.

15 See 14 above.

16 See 14 above.

17 Villareal S F, McKinney LE, Quakenbush M, *Handle with Care: Helping children* prenatally exposed to drugs and alcohol, Santa Cruz, California, ETR Associates, 1991, USA.

18 Gittler J, and McPherson M, 'Prenatal Substance Abuse: An overview of the problem', *Children Today* 19 (4): 3-7, 1990, USA.

19 Rist M C, 'Crack Babies at School' *The American School Board Journal*, January 1990, USA.

20 See 9 above.

21 See 10 above.

22 Fanshel D, 'Parental Failure and Consequences for Children' *American Journal of Public Health* 65 (6): 604612, June 1975, USA.

23 Zuckerman B, and Frank D A, 'Crack Kids: Not Broken', *Pediatrics* 24 (89): 337-339, 1992, USA.

24 Mayes L, Granger R H, et al, 'The Problem of Prenatal Cocaine Exposure: A rush to judgement' *Journal of the American Medical Association* 267 (3): 406-408, 1992, USA.

3 Roadmaps and decoders
Helping children exposed to parental substance abuse

There are a number of areas where parents of substance-affected children find their children often run into problems. In many cases, traditional ways of dealing with these, and traditional teaching and discipline don't seem to be effective in helping children. The refrain heard is "He/she keeps making the same mistakes!" We keep trying, and they try harder, but in some areas there is still a lot of frustration. We could help our children learn more effectively in some cases if we could remember that it's not always just putting in *more* effort, but putting in effort *differently*.

Many children affected by parental substance abuse have difficulties learning in traditional ways because they learn differently. This is the disability: they do not learn as well as other children do when using traditional teaching methods. Much teaching in primary schools still consists of the teacher talking at children, and the children being expected to sit quietly, remember, and write things down. Receiving information through listening, and translating it into writing or behaviour, is one of the areas where many substance-affected children have great difficulty. Receiving information and then returning appropriate verbal or behavioural responses can be difficult. For some children, their intelligence levels may be high, but their skill levels may not be in processing information.

Since children exposed to parental substance abuse have such a wide range of intellectual abilities and learning differences, it is hard to make more than sweeping generalisations when discussing their needs. What is presented here are some potential areas of difficulty for some children, and some possible responses.

Children who learn differently may depend more heavily on their other senses, senses which are not utilised as often in schools as those used for listening, reading, and writing. Pre-school programmes and the early grades may use physical activities, concrete materials, and acting out information as ways to help children learn. In these early education settings teachers recognise the needs of children to use all of their senses to receive and reinforce new data, and use their whole bodies to experience learning. But children in the upper forms are more often required to sit in one place, sort out lots of different noises and sounds, and reproduce information upon request. The higher the grade level, the more complex and abstract the concepts. The higher the grade level, the more children are expected to stick to their desks. The less concrete the information and activities, the more difficult it is to deal with for many children.

Most children use words that they hear as building blocks in communication, which are put together to give meaning, and taken apart and repositioned to send information back. For children with information processing deficits, spoken words instead become barriers that block understanding, and take a long time to decode and figure out. Other children may receive information well, but have difficulty formulating messages for responses.

Problems like these can cause enormous frustration for children, and for their parents and teachers. "You could do it if you really tried," a child hears. Or even more devastating, "You could do it if you really wanted to." What happens when a child really is trying and really does want to succeed, but can't succeed with this task? Depending on the child and the kind of supports the child is receiving, it can mean depression, temper tantrums, stress overload, more fuel for a negative self-image, or help to rethink the task and the ways of approaching it.

The problems increase in secondary school, where students are expected to use abstract reasoning and higher mathematical skills. Students can feel they are working harder and harder with less success. Problems with poor social judgement and poor consequencing skills can lead some adolescents into difficult if not dangerous situations. Some teenagers may be more vulnerable to emotional, financial, or sexual victimisation because of these problems.

Developing learning skills
Children with more subtle learning differences can still have difficulty relating one piece of information to the other. Despite normal intelligence

and higher IQ scores, they may still need more external supports and more techniques and cues in the environment than other children their age are expected to use. Since they tend to be more visual in their information processing, they often need visual or concrete prompts combined with verbal instructions.

Some children have difficulty integrating what they already know with new information to build skills. Or they do well on a task one day but seem to forget what to do the next day. Problems with uneven memory and inconsistent performance can be frustrating for children and for those helping them. Children with these types of problems may need a lot of repetition, cues, and prompts to reinforce patterns of learning; they may need these refreshed, reviewed, and rechecked later to make sure it stays in their internal memory banks.

Learning that engages the child physically and uses more than one sense can help reinforce information. When the whole child, with many senses, is engaged in learning, and the whole body is responding in the learning experience, more information is likely to be retained for a longer period of time for many children.

For many children, verbal information is the least likely to be retained. This is a problem since so much teaching is done with children listening. Children may be able to parrot back what is said, but it may take longer to decode what those received words mean. Or the words may not be properly decoded at all. On the other hand, many children with poor verbal memory have very good visual memory, which can be used to strengthen their learning tasks.

People have referred to the task of memory storage for FAS/FAE children, in particular, as a "computer bank that hiccups" or a wardrobe where things are jumbled together because the hangers don't always stay up. These traits make it difficult for adults to accept that children are really trying to work and co-operate, and aren't lazy or oppositional. After all, if a child does well one day, why should he or she do poorly the next day on the same task or memory? This causes more frustration to add to the frustration children already experience.

Experienced parents point to a number of common problems and some of the ways to tackle these. They emphasise that each child, parent, family, and teacher are different, even from day to day. What works for one or on one day may not the next. Flexibility is a key word, but flexibility within a regular, consistent routine. Whether they like it or not, knowing what to expect puts less stress on a child, and lowered stress levels mean a child is less likely to be flooded and overreact, and more likely to be able to focus and concentrate.

Children who have been in chaotic or negative environments before coming into the family may resist structure and rules even though they may need them desperately. Children struggling with emotional issues can have many of the same stress and overload reactions as children with organically based problems. When these two factors come together, the impact can increase geometrically. Addressing just one of the issues involved with their emotional or learning difficulties won't be as effective in helping the child learn how to cope with the presenting problems.

So much of the child's life at home, and especially at school, is more complicated for a child with the burden of an emotional or a physical residue from parental substance abuse. Even in programmes that recognise the child's special needs, the emphasis is so often on the weak areas, fixing on what is wrong. The primary focus is on what the child can't do that has to be changed. Too often there is little or no recognition of the *whole* child. Seldom do we look at the very real frustration and other emotional reactions to these learning disabilities and differences.

Parents fall into the same trap: we are so occupied with immediate behaviour problems and preoccupied with what has to be done (or what we think ought to be done) that we do not highlight the child's strengths, such as interests beyond the classroom and talents that could be recognised and nurtured and enjoyed. So often adults are too busy looking at what's wrong that we don't celebrate what is right. We don't take the time to teach children to find and take pride in these parts of themselves. Professionals and parents worry about reaching goals, and overcoming obstacles, and uncertain futures. We don't take time to enjoy the present, the positive, the fun of this child.

Since schools are among the least likely places to do this, parents have to be especially sensitive to these needs and ways in which to address them. No child likes to be labelled all the time as the slow one. Even within the family, the unspoken – or even spoken – designation might be a negative tag like the problem child, the drag, the one who is always embarrassing us. Without even realising it, resentments and frustration pile up.

Children with strong emotional needs and learning differences need, perhaps even more than children who have an easier time feeling secure and capable, to find people and interests where they can have a good time and feel good about themselves. They don't have to excel, just enjoy. An interest in collecting matchbox cars or keeping up with teenage fashion can provide positives like release from tension, knowledge to share with others (and perhaps exceed others at times), and practice in remembering information. Since many children with learning differences go at their own pace and with their own style that can be different from peers, team sports and competitive situations aren't always a good match for all children. But more individual pursuits, especially those where you can set your own goals and increase proficiency at your own pace, can be helpful. Swimming, dance, gymnastics, aerobics, weightlifting, athletics, and martial arts are some examples. Some interests and hobbies can set a pattern for life-long knowledge and enjoyment, sharing with others, or perhaps skills or experiences in disciplined behaviour to build on for careers: cooking, gardening, carpentry, art, working on cars, music, sewing, and pets are just a few.

Children need opportunities to try, to fail, and also to succeed. They need support to learn, and support to grow emotionally healthy. For children with special needs who learn differently, it is not just trying harder by children and adults: we will also have to learn different ways, including joyful ways, to encourage their healthy learning and growing.

Some general tips from experienced parents for parents

- Keep your child in perspective within the whole family: remember that your child with special needs is only *one* member. Make sure everyone gets their time, including parents. Make time for good times.
- Keep your child's special needs in perspective by keeping the whole child in mind, trying to balance all aspects of your growing child: talents and limits, physical, emotional, medical, educational, and spiritual needs.
- Simplify your lifestyle and home environment and keep your daily routines consistent and structured: make rules in your family short and

clear, write down chores, keep a calendar posted, eliminate clutter and have set places for things; use visual cues and reminders.

- Use "Slowly" and "Calm" as key words when your child is stressed and when you are stressed.

- Be creative and be willing to be flexible in figuring out how to help a child cope with a problem or how to cope with a problem child. Break tasks down into small steps.

- Typical discipline and learning techniques that work well with other children in your family may only lead to frustration with a child with special needs. Some of these may include: contracting, behaviour modification, asking why, explaining why, saying "Just keep trying".

- Trust your instincts; you know your child best.

- Plan for long-term goals while enjoying the present fully.

- Delegate: you are not superparent. At home and in the community, find places and people to help your child feel good and succeed, as well as finding coping strategies.

- Keep communication open. This holds true within your family, between parents and parents and children, and also between the various people and services working with your child. This is related to keeping the whole child in perspective, rather than fragmented parts of the child.

- Find ways for your children to succeed and have interests beyond the pressures of what they have trouble with.

- Find ways for you as parent to do likewise.

Hyperactivity

Hyperactivity can have an organic basis or an emotional basis, but even organically based hyperactivity can be aggravated by emotional factors. Any of this can aggravate adults. Hyperactive children don't have to experience negative emotions to become overstressed. Positive experiences can also cause overload. Think about a group of children at a birthday party. Picture a dozen excited children anticipating the gifts inside brightly wrapped packages, eating ice cream and cake loaded with sugar, running around during games and between games, becoming sweaty, overheated, and overexcited. Even the placid withdrawn child can look a little flushed. Now zoom in to focus on the truly hyperactive child. Despite the fun atmosphere, this child has probably speeded up his or her activity level greatly and is having trouble paying attention to any particular activity, because too many stimuli – noise, music, colour, food, numbers of people – are beginning to blur everything together into a frantic whirl causing the child to speed up more. Sooner or later, unless an adult intervenes to help the child de-escalate the level of stimulation and activity, this child is bound to run into trouble . . . probably literally.

This kind of activity level is not popular with teachers and others who are required to keep groups of children on task. The fact that the child may not physically be able to maintain more appropriate behaviour may be sympathetically appreciated, but still be problematic. Medication is one possibility, but is not appropriate for all children. For some children medication can literally be lifesaving; for a child without the ability to maintain safe behaviour, not using medication might be like withholding insulin for a child with diabetes. For other children, medication is just one part of the total plan to help the child with feelings and behaviours.

Whether or not medication is a part of the plan, a variety of strategies, alternatives, and tools usually need to be available to effectively parent the child with hyperactive behaviour and feelings, and to effectively teach this child.

Talk with other parents and with professionals about what has worked and hasn't worked for them. Try out a few of their suggestions that look like they may fit the unique combination of your parenting style and your child's particular needs. Modify what doesn't work, and change things around to suit your family.

Suggestions on coping with hyperactivity

- Environmental modification: the child's space in the classroom and at home should be as simple and structured as possible, with few distractions. Limit the number of toys, clothes, pictures, bright lighting, noise, etc.
- Environmental modification: keep items in the classroom and at home in the same place.
- To alleviate stress: keep the child cued into what is happening with a simple daily schedule and weekly calendar.
- Provide quiet places: defined spaces that are private yet close to people,

like a chair turned around with a towel blocking the view, or a separate room with access to adults. Practise using this spot a few minutes every day after school to unwind from the day.

- Provide calming alternatives that the child can gradually learn to use on his/her own: soft music on a walkman (try lullabies, nature music, classics, love songs or slow dance music), slowly and softly brushing a pet or stuffed animal (at first under supervision), dimming the lights, *slowly* rocking in a rocking chair or swing (back and forth is more calming to many kids than side to side).

- Talk and breathe more calmly and slowly; teach the child to breathe in deeply and let the breath out slowly.

- Look for the triggers, stimuli, situations for out of control behaviour and try out ways to avoid them, find alternatives, or cope with them in better ways.

- What is soothing for one child may be distracting for another . . . or for parents or teachers, for that matter.

- Limit things that escalate excitement levels; ration these items when children can appropriately let off steam afterwards, like running outside. Television, videos, and popular music are big culprits here. Instead of action adventure movies with fast chases and violence, sitcoms with frantic laugh tracks, and music videos full of aggression and sex, try nature shows, Disney Movies, and calmer music.

- If a situation has built-in stressors, like school exams, the class play, or birthdays, try to keep other stressors, including the number of people, to a minimum.

- Try to get an extra adult or mature teenager to help out or to engage one-to-one with the stress prone child.

- Prepare for "crash time", with calm and quiet, after activities with lots of stimuli or stress.

- Leave time between stimulating activities, plan to alternate these with calmer events.

- If a child is cycling up, you may be able to pull them back to ground level with a gentle intervention. Put a hand softly on their shoulder (this grounds the child physically and connects non-verbally with the speaker) and then talk in a low, soft but clear voice close to their ear.

- Get the child's attention by using their name first, then with a minimum of words – preferably using the same key phrases each time – tell him or her what your concern is ("I see that you are getting noisy," or "It bothers me that you are losing control") and make a simple suggestion about how to get into control again ("Breathe deeply four times," or "Set the timer for one minute and use the Quiet Place"). This is not a punishment but a reminder of how the child has the ability to get back into control on his/her own.

- In some situations, instead of trying to squash the behaviour like pushing a jack in the box on springs back into a tight space, try to find another outlet for excess energy and emotions, preferably a focused physical activity that uses large muscles, like running around the table. Tell children to use up their extra energy so that they can give more attention when they come back. Aggressive activities are not advisable, since these only seem to increase aggression.

- Children who are very active, not well co-ordinated or very distractible will need more adult structure and supervision and more time and space to be able to stay on target in tasks, and also for de-stress or calming.

- Structure in some "energy breaks" every day, just like adults schedule coffee breaks, to give the child a change in physical location and activity, and to break rising stress levels: check the letterbox, or say hello the same time each day in the principal's office, or walk the dog. You may need extra breaks too.

- Try a quiet place or quiet time for yourself; find time to be by yourself and with other adults to maintain your sanity. Invest in industrial strength babysitters, not only for regular once a week getaways but once or twice weekly for at least half an hour. Try teenagers from big families or who have hyperactive siblings, or special education students. When you can't escape and children are cheerfully or not so cheerfully wound up, try using the walkman yourself.

Stress overload

Children who are overloaded often seem to short circuit. They can escalate hyper or negative behaviour to anger or panic or do an emotional shutdown, where rational communication seems to be impossible. Their intellectual, emotional, and sometimes even physical, responses may become rigid. Children can get locked into repeating the same behaviours or phrases over and over again, despite the fact that these are not working in this situation. While some children may physically withdraw, run away from the situation, or sleep for long periods of time, others may talk in louder voices, yell, or have full blown temper tantrums; a few children may have laboured breathing or talk in monotones, like a machine that has gone into automatic pilot.

When children display these behaviours, people can feel under attack, feel shut out, or feel children are deliberately defying them. The adult response is usually to try harder to get through to the child, to regain contact through touch, to keep talking, or to attempt to get compliance from the child through logical consequences or plain old-fashioned threats of punishment.

All of these approaches, even the compassionate and usually appropriate calm touch and rational talking, often backfire for a child whose internal computer has said "That's it! No more messages of any kind are coming in!". If strong emotions like anger or fear are involved, remember that someone in the middle of the adrenaline rush of strong negative emotions can be like someone on drugs: the powerful surge of emotions can block out normal abilities to think clearly. For some children in these situations, the very strategies we successfully use at other times may instead increase the child's distress at not being able to receive messages clearly: more words and added touch can mean more stimuli loaded on to an already overloaded system. Like adding more soap and more clothes when the washer isn't working properly, well-meaning concern can instead lead to an explosion or breakdown.

The most important things for adults to keep in mind in situations like this are: the problem doesn't have to be solved right now; and this child is flooded and frightened. Since you need to reduce the outside stimulation before the child can deal with the inner overload, first deal with things in the environment, like noise or other children, before you try out stress reducers with the child. Assess which work best for your child and practise them together *before* using them when situations get hot.

Coping with overload
- Back off: resist the urge to jump in, fix it or talk it out. Slow down

your own responses to the situation.

- Children often pick up on an adult's heightened emotional responses, which can escalate their own rising emotions. Try to detach somewhat, breathe slowly, and relax before deciding how you will intervene.
- Accept the child's decision that this is a situation where he or she can go no further right now. If the child still has space to hear you, acknowledge with: "This is not okay for you. Stop and just breathe now."
- Decide if this is a good situation for physical and emotional space to safely blow off energy and emotion. Redirect to acceptable outlets that you can supervise.
- Decide if this is a good situation for time and space to physically and emotionally hide out. Would the child be able to appropriately use a Quiet Place or Quiet Time? Would the child need you to supervise, or need you somewhat close (but not in their space) to feel safe?
- Give the child a time to vent, and accept these as real feelings even if you disagree with the reasons or the behaviour that followed ("I see you have very strong feelings," or "You feel really upset"). Set limits on how the feelings are expressed, however, no aggression. Save solutions for well after the emotional level has dropped.
- Practise the techniques and strategies you want to try for overload *before* an overload situation occurs. You can't teach an exercise for tension release, for example, when children are so tense they block out communication.
- Try different ways to use techniques, especially ways that go beyond just talking, and ways that use more than one sense. For example, for the typical breathing exercise that has a child take and release deep breaths slowly, one parent holds up fingers or holds the child's fingers against the diaphragm for "magic counting" of breaths.
- Teach children to recognise their own signs of stress, and different ways to reduce these. Practise.

Suggestions about coping with change
- Explain changes in advance to a child, but within the specific child's level of tolerance for anticipation.
- Explain changes using a minimum of words, and reinforce this using

other senses (such as looking at or drawing pictures, acting things out or using models).

- Teach and practise recognising stress signals and using different de-stress tools. Assess at which points children are most likely to feel most stressed, and practise going through these and using tools.

- Use "cue" words or phrases or sign language to help children remember. Practise these; write or draw them on post-it notes placed on lunchboxes, coats, refrigerator doors, wherever children are most likely to see them (but not if the child is embarrassed in front of others).

- Things that use concrete objects or examples to explain about the change are most helpful.

- Things which concretely demonstrate the sequence or timing of changes are also very helpful: an egg timer that ticks off minutes or seconds; a digital clock; a calendar with days crossed off; removing one object from a calendar or clock for each segment of time.

- As with most things, what will work for one child may not with another. One child may respond well to wearing a watch, for example, while another will forget to look at it and feel frustrated. Be creative; involve the child in figuring out alternatives. ("What if . . .?")

- The more changes, the higher the stress. If at all possible, try to stagger the timing of changes.

- When multiple changes must occur, make sure concrete cues are posted and accessible, such as pictures, calendars, timetables, schedules. Try cue cards made from index cards or sticky-backed paper name tags or bookmarks. Have children paste a list on the back of their morning cereal box. Try short audiotapes with the reminders of sequences or steps in a poem, chant, rap, or song.

- Break things down into smaller segments. Give a child index cards with these listed for the child to hold.

- Before a change, de-stress children by alternating required tasks with relaxing or calming activities and activities which allow for physical release of energy.

- Help children make a chart with the new schedule or a map with the new directions, and encourage them to be creative. Use pasting, cutting, and stickers as well as pencils and crayons. Make your own also, based on theirs, to post. (Especially if there is more than one child, yours may be clearer to refer to, but acknowledge that you got your ideas from them and be willing to make corrections.)

- If possible, physically walk children through a change at least once or twice before the time of the change: try out the way to the new classroom or school, practise what you will say to the new teacher, go look at and walk around in the new neighbourhood.

- When possible, give graduated warnings or preparation for a change in activity ("It's five minutes until gym, put books away . . . It's three minutes until gym, etc.) Use related physical cues for the change (like a raised hand) or for the activity (like a book or a lunchbag).

- Have the children write down the steps, then say them aloud. Try putting the steps to rhythm, a nursery rhyme, or music. Try clapping hands or tapping the desk as you chant the steps out loud.

- Give children a time to vent their negative feelings and fears. Even if they don't seem reasonable to you, they are very real to the children. Reinforce the right ways to deal with feelings and correct inappropriate behaviours.

- Talk with children about what little things they are worried about and what worries them most. Accept these are real, don't discount them, and together discuss ways to deal with the problems or the feelings. Ask children directly: "What would make you feel safer (or more grownup, or less worried, or whatever the fear is) in this situation?"; "What can you do to figure this out?"; "How can I help?"; "Who else could help?"

- Teach children to "brainstorm", which is to make a list out loud of possible options and solutions straight from the top of your head, no thinking about it. Tell the children they must add silly or fantasy reasons and wishes as well as real solutions. In addition to teaching a way to discuss alternative solutions, this can release tension, uncover feelings and desires, and turn up creative and unexpected options. It can also enhance children's self-esteem by being listened to and having their input respected. And it can be fun!

Touch and bonding

Children exposed to parental substance abuse can have a number of difficult issues related to touch and to bonding. If they have lived in chaotic or neglectful environments, made many moves, or experienced physical and/or sexual abuse, these emotional issues can interfere with developing a healthy sense of touch, with trust, and with attachments. A child with prenatal effects that cause hypersensitivity to stimuli and difficulty processing information can have difficulty in this too. When both of these factors, environmental and genetic, are in place, the impact can be many times greater.

Because of these issues, touch as a positive part of the natural human interaction between child and adult, and of the whole process of making positive human connections called attachment, becomes more difficult for a child exposed to prenatal substance abuse. Sometimes the very things adults do to lovingly soothe, comfort, and nurture children are instead perceived by a child as irritants, which interfere with the attachment process. Rocking side to side, cuddling, eye contact, labels on clothing, light from the window or lamp, lullabies and even a parent's voice may all be potential irritants to a hypersensitive or tactile defensive child.

A hypersensitive baby may be irritable, difficult to hold or calm, and make both days and nights a trial in patience for the carers. A hypersensitive toddler may resist cuddling, or cheerful mobiles and toys bought especially by the parent, or have frequent temper tantrums. An older child who can't seem to make eye contact, doesn't want to be touched but clings or is inappropriate, and can't seem to follow directions, is usually not the child the parent dreamed of. Parents feel deprived of sharing their love and receiving in turn, and children feel more and more deprived of what they really need to grow healthy.

Instead of coming closer, the child pushes away. Instead of feeling closer, the adult feels frustrated and rejected. Without intervention, the cycle can continue to spiral into frustration, aggression, or depression. Since these children often can't actively show what they need or how to break through to get it, parents have to take the initiative. Gently but firmly, hypersensitive or traumatised children have to be taught to trust or to trust again. They need to slowly find safe ways to accept and even seek out healthy touch and positive human connections. Parents may need to experiment until the right combinations are found for their child, but the effort is well worth it.

Suggestions on encouraging touch and bonding

- Reduce to a minimum what seems to bother the child: clothing, blankets, and certain textures; avoid ruffles, smocking, and other detailing; try fabric softener; remove labels; keep a softer layer between the child's skin and the necessary but irritating garment, like snowsuits.

- Paradoxically, some infants respond to swaddling, being wrapped so securely they can't easily move.

- Try dimmer, indirect lighting and reduce the noise level. To block out sounds or attempt to calm, try very soft, calm, nature sounds or "white noise".

- Simplify the child's room and environment: keep toys, clothing, pictures to an absolute minimum and avoid loud colours and noises, mobiles, etc.

- If the child rejects foods, check with a doctor, nurse, or nutritionist to find things the child will accept.

- With an older child resistant to touch, give verbal warning and a short description of the touch beforehand: "We hold hands crossing the street," or "I'm going to give you an okay hug," or "It's time to kiss you goodnight".

- Some professionals suggest asking a child's permission to touch but a number of parents point out they wouldn't get anywhere if they had to wait for that; instead they suggest you start by very briefly and simply defining what is okay touch for children and parents, and then assure children that is the only kind of touch you will give. Afterwards, reinforce with descriptions as above.

- To start to establish comfortable eye contact, first get down to the child's level so you are eye to eye. Use simple short words to describe ("I like to look at you, I'm glad you live here."); reinforce with a light touch on the shoulder. Start with only a few seconds at a time.

- Some parents find that humour works well with some older children but not with others who are very concrete. For example, one child only allowed her new Dad to shake hands. At bedtime, he shook her toe goodnight, making her giggle about this silly but safe touch.

Lying, stealing, and other poor social skills

Children exposed to parental substance abuse may display negative behaviour because of emotional problems related to attachment, separation and loss, or abuse. They also may not have learned appropriate behaviour in earlier placements. Learning problems may make it difficult for them to learn or remember to use good social judgement. Stress may cause children to forget or ignore behaviour rules they already know.

Sometimes children who are intrusive or invasive are reflecting experiences related to physical or sexual abuse, but for other children prenatal damage makes abstract concepts like body space, personal boundaries, truth, and personal possessions very difficult indeed. The ways that you help children with these issues differ depending upon what the causal factors are and what is influencing these now. This is very tricky, for professionals as well as parents and carers. Given information about the possibilities and symptoms, parents usually develop good instincts about possible issues for their children.

For children with developmental delays, behaviours may reflect understanding at much younger levels than their chronological age. Age-inappropriate behaviour for them may be very appropriate for their developmental level. For example, a child may be operating at the self-centred stage of a preschooler. Another child may not understand the relationship between an object and its owner when that person is not physically present.

In the past, stealing and lying were considered signs of a lack of conscience for most children. But for many FAS children in particular, the actions were not deliberately devious but demonstrating the inability of these children to process information fully at all times. Lying, for example, may not always be a deliberate attempt to deceive. When lying is glaringly obvious it may be a symptom of memory problems instead. "Confabulation" is the term used to describe the kind of "storytelling" that a person may use (often unconsciously) to answer a question when there are gaps in information or memory. The person simply fills in the gaps with whatever ready information comes to mind, plausible or not. It may become a habit which seems easier than pushing the mind to retrieve lost information or admitting you don't know. In many ways it can be an imperfect defence mechanism rather than deliberate misbehaviour.

Suggestions about dealing with lying, stealing, and intrusive behaviour

- Make the abstract concepts of body space and boundaries more real and concrete through practical examples and activities: draw body outlines with "body halos" around them coloured in to indicate private space; demonstrate safety circles/privacy circles with your arms held out: string yarn around a bed, desk, chair, or other "invaded territory" to show what is off limits; tape lines across bedrooms or around other personal space.
- Make a limited number of clear, simple rules about personal boundaries, and discuss them briefly with family members. Put them in a written list for children to read. Include touching, looking, privacy, bedrooms and bathrooms, personal property and space, and consequences.
- Model and then practise; use puppets, dolls, or role play to practise appropriate behaviour.
- Provide "cue cards": use index cards with short steps in simple language for specific situations. Go over the steps before these situations are likely to occur.
- Make a family rule "No finding things". If you or a child does find something, firmly show how to return it.
- If you know a child is lying or stealing, don't ask if he or she is lying or stealing. Instead, say "I don't think that is the true story. Think about what the true story is," or "I know that isn't yours. How do you plan to return or replace it?"
- If you know boundary issues are problematic, provide consistent supervision and don't provoke situations by letting rules slide or, for example, leaving money out.
- Instead of punishment, think in terms of teaching opportunities. When a child must be closely supervised because of inappropriate behaviour, for example, instead of the usual "You have bad behaviour, you are punished by being grounded," communicate to the child your concern, tell how you will help keep him/her safe and teach okay behaviour,

and share your confidence that they will eventually learn the behaviour: "I care about you, so I will keep you safe where I can see you, while you learn and practise (insert the correct behaviour to be worked on). You're smart, I know you'll learn fast."

- Try to avoid situations where the child will probably make up an answer if he or she doesn't know or is in the wrong.

Auditory comprehension and speech

A number of problems for children affected by prenatal substance abuse centre on language. Children may have missed important developmental steps because they were focused on survival. Children who come from chaotic or neglectful backgrounds or had many moves in foster care may not have had adults consistently pay attention to tasks like appropriate speech, pronunciation, or grammar. Children emotionally affected by parental substance abuse may have problems when the words they learned earlier may not mean the same things in your home. A child who has been sexually abused may have learned that men labelled as "Dad" or "Uncle" (or all men) are abusive. In your family these words probably mean a loving person who uses his strengths to protect and comfort. The word "love" may have been used when "sex" would have been the more appropriate word. As in an overseas adoption, this child coming into your home may have a different language and set of customs, some of which come into conflict with your understanding and values.

There are also organically based language difficulties common to many children exposed to parental substance abuse, which can contribute to other problems in addition to developmental or academic concerns. For example, if a child's expressive language – how he or she communicates verbally to others – is stronger than their receptive language – how they make sense of the spoken words used in communication – then social and behavioural difficulties emerge. People see a verbal, even chatty, child, and assume this child will of course understand. But the ability to understand and process the incoming information well enough to act on it in the correct way is not as strong as their speech. Often the rapid flow of words and a friendly manner prevents people from realising that the speech, comprehension and behaviour levels don't match up for this child.

Children could also have other types of information processing difficulties related to language. For cocaine-exposed children, in particular, expressive language is the problem. They understand what they hear, but may have difficulties sending information back to you. Where most children use words as building blocks in communication, children with receptive language processing skills often find words more confusing than clarifying. Words become barriers, blocking understanding instead of being building blocks. Parents and professionals have shared that for some children, the more you talk, the less likely the child is to understand. When children don't understand, the natural response is to explain further, using more verbal explanations. But for children with difficulty processing verbal language received, these words just keep piling up in front of the child, obscuring the original question. Children may smile and nod to prevent embarrassment or consequences and stop the flow of words they are trying to block out. Or they may go into stress overload because they are just too overwhelmed by this overabundance of verbal stimuli. When children look glazed or frustrated, or you are just not sure that smiling face really understands, it's best to stop, not keep explaining. Take a break, start again, try communication using more than one sensory avenue to get your message across.

For some children, especially children with significant speech or language problems, concrete visual cues can help a child focus better on the message symbolised by the words. Sign language has proven to be especially helpful. It can act as a bridge between expressive and receptive language. By increasing the child's access to the meaning of language and the words for objects and concepts it deepens the child's abilities in vocabulary and comprehension.

Deaf children who learn sign language at an early age and later learn written and oral English have been shown to have far more sophisticated grasp of language and greatly increased vocabulary in both sign and English than deaf children only exposed to English. This disproves concerns from some who felt that sign might discourage children's grasp of spoken language. For deaf children and for hearing children with speech and language problems the opposite has proven to be true. Sign used in combination with English has provided opportunities to keep language growing and help with decoding when verbal language is still not a proficient skill. Parents have also found that signs provide a discreet avenue for giving children cues and reminders.

For some children the mechanics of speech may present a problem. There may be physical or developmental reasons why certain sounds are difficult. Children with delayed development may need extra help to improve speech patterns, increase vocabulary, and pronounce words clearly and correctly.

Games, stories, nursery rhymes and songs may seem like simple routines for children but they are important ways adults help children develop a sense of the flow and interaction of language. For children with learning differences, the repetition and rhyme of these are very helpful reinforcers. The sharing of these within the family is also a positive way children can learn to feel safe and develop trust with adults who care about them. Taking time to sit close and cuddle while looking at the pictures in books, being silly, hopping, jumping and clapping, and singing together as you work together not only uses the child's whole body and senses to learn about language, but also helps in learning about feeling good, being close, and trust.

Suggestions on improving auditory skills and spoken language

- Basic strategy: keep a structured routine and environment to cut down distractions and dealing with new things.
- Break down information into smaller segments or steps.
- Use body language and touch, but be clear about appropriate touching and about personal boundaries.
- Visual thinking is often the stronger skill for children with auditory processing difficulties. Use artwork, the written word, and other ways to help children get a visual image, especially for more abstract ideas.
- Use concrete, physical demonstrations or cues along with or instead of verbal messages (pictures, photos, lists, words in boxes, post-it notes and reminders; acting out or using models; sign language and cues; and so on).
- When talking, use clear precise language in short sentences. Use a minimum of words at the child's level.
- Don't be tempted to give lectures or long explanations. Stop, work out how to break up the message into manageable size bites, and put

it aside for later if it isn't working now.

- Children are often literal thinkers: be careful of slang, sayings, or exaggerations. ("No, I'm not really going to give him a piece of my mind. I'll keep my brain inside my head and just talk to him.")
- Other stimuli in the environment may be distracting a child from paying attention to or expressing verbal messages. Just as other sensory avenues can help a child with information, they can also get in the way. A child may not be able to easily filter out noise, smell, lights, bright colours, other activities or people, a scratchy label, or even the taste of their sweets. Overload is easier for a distractible child. Try to figure out what that wiggling is about. You may need to make a space more free from as many of these distractions as possible before you can focus a child appropriately.
- Whenever possible, use the positive form rather than the negative form of verbal language: say "Please talk quietly," or "We only give good touch," instead of "Don't yell," or "Don't hurt." Not only is it better emotionally and tells children directly what is expected, it also has fewer words to confuse a child.
- Since emotions can easily confuse or overstimulate a child and block communication, try to recognise potential overload situations and try to deflect them. Teach children to recognise and label emotions and stress signs and use appropriate behaviour to deal with these.
- Once overload is reached for you or the child, back off and take a break. Don't keep trying to communicate or fix it.
- Children who do not have appropriate words available to them may not be able to describe or make sense of their environment, especially related to feelings. Teach new words reinforced by physical cues and sign language.
- If a child is able to comfortably make eye contact or accept simple touch like hand on the shoulder, use these to signal and help a child to focus on your message.
- Try to use the same words and sequences or patterns when giving directions, especially for emergencies.
- Try to use the same visual or physical cues for situations each time these arise. Start with just one or two before you increase these in number and complexity.

- Give reminders using a single word as a cue, rather than repeating the whole message or the reasons why. For example, instead of going through another explanation of why towels need to picked up or how you have reminded your child before, save breath and energy and prevent "parent deafness" merely saying "Towel" and pointing. You may need to use a *very* brief explanation at first, but afterwards just repeat the word if necessary.
- Sign language can be fun for siblings or parents to learn. Sometimes it's fun for the child with learning differences to find something at which they are more proficient than the rest of the family or that they can teach.
- In addition to helping with language and providing visual cues and reminders, sign language can also provide subtle reminders between family members or parent and child for messages like slow down, lower the noise level, this is silly stuff, or your fly is unzipped. Enjoy it and appreciate its richness.
- Take time to enjoy the many forms of expression. Find ways your children can express creativity and communicate through these, to expand and enrich their lives. Find time on your own and with your child to stop and smell flowers, cook tasty food, look at sunsets, make music, share feelings, and hold hands. Teach your child to live fully and with appreciation for the many gifts life has to offer.

Other suggestions on language
- Since working on areas where there are problems or gaps can be stressful, some of the suggestions below deal with how to avoid stress. Plan to do these activities at the time, pace and place that is comfortable for both of you.
- Get suggestions from teachers, speech therapists and parents. Instead of formal exercises, adapt these into fun times together. For example, instead of just repeating the "p" sound, practise tongue twisters together, make up silly sentences with "p" words, and make up a game finding "p" words while driving in the car.
- Keep both the child's developmental level and interests in mind. A child may be emotionally or intellectually behind other children, or just need time to repeat familiar things. Keep it light and fun for both of you.

- Keep within the child's sense of time. You know your child best and how long your child can sit still or focus at any one given time. Keep your activities well within that time frame and increase slowly.
- Repetition can drive parents wild but it is important to children. For children with learning differences repetition is especially helpful. Stories, games, poems and songs that repeat things can bore adults but delight children while reinforcing learning.
- Make the transition to other activity levels or activities slowly; it's best not to do too much or too many different activities at any one time.
- Simple baby and child games that encourage language, like nursery rhymes, also teach skills like sequencing, cause and effect, paying attention, and trust. With older kids who still need or want these, make it silly and fun, or encourage them to help younger children (under supervision).
- Make corrections matter of factly, without a lot of attention to mistakes. Instead of global praise note, in a low key way, the specific positive step made.

4 The challenges of parenting
What works for my family

Liz Grimes

For me, one of the primary aims in parenting is to have children able to understand their environment and manage their own behaviour within realistic boundaries, with as little direct adult supervision as possible. Another, perhaps more important goal, is to convey to children an encouraging, positive attitude. Each child is capable of reaching realistic goals successfully when he or she has others who care about them as important people.

Children exposed to alcohol and drugs often function better when parents are able to provide:

- Models of the desired behaviour
- Consistency of expectations and predictability of routines and responses (with parental persistence)
- Planning and structuring of environment, rules, and activities
- Acceptance and acknowledgement of their efforts, with reinforcements and rewards
- Clear and concise communication with positive attitudes

When these are in place, adults can be more secure in their parenting and children can be more secure within their families. Without this sense of security, children do not have the emotional energy to put in the extra effort required for coping within the family and in the community. When parents can provide a family environment based firmly on important values and supported through skills and strategies like these, children don't have to worry so much about basic survival issues and are free to put more of themselves into the many difficult tasks facing them. Parents are also freed from having to make new decisions with every new situation.

These particular issues now outlined are what have been most important for my husband Jac and I in parenting our family. Hopefully, some of these will be helpful to you as well.

Modelling

Modelling behaviours works with young children as well as with older children and teenagers. Children need to see adults using appropriate behaviour. So, don't let a child see or hear you doing something that you do not want a child to do. For example, don't ask a child to say you are not home when you are, if you don't want a child to lie. Don't use spanking or hitting as a means of punishment if kids are not allowed to hit others. Here are some general steps on how you could use modelling:

- Tell the child the behaviour you desire.
- Show the child the behaviour.
- Let the child show you the behaviour.
- Follow up to see if the behaviour is consistently completed, and correct or reinforce as necessary.

Here is one example of modelling:

Situation: Clothes in the hamper.

Helpful response: "In this house we put our dirty clothes, that we wore today, in the laundry hamper."

Non-helpful response: "Pick up your clothes:"

This modelling situation isn't finished until the followup: the parent checks that the laundry is placed in the hamper (otherwise the kids may decide that you are satisfied with their clothes on the floor). Have the children show you how they can put their laundry in the hamper correctly, and keep checking.

Here is another example:

Situation: Petting the dog.

Helpful response: "We pet the dog gently on her back. Here is how we pet her back. Help me pet her on her back."

Non-helpful response: "Don't hit the dog, pet her right!"

Use as many of the child's senses as possible: tell, show, and do. The more physically involved children are, the more likely they are to be able to repeat the behaviour.

Consistency and predictability

It is much easier to say "Be consistent" than it is to actually be consistent. Children will often do everything in their power to wear you down so that you will not be able to do what you tell them you will do. Because others who don't understand your children's needs often frown on necessary consequences, you may feel like letting targeted behaviour slide, even when you know you can't. Children have a way of knowing just when those times are and will choose them as times to try you. Therefore, it is important that you say what you mean and mean what you say.

It is also necessary to solicit the assistance of other important people in the child's life to be equally consistent with the child. For example, teachers need to know what behaviours you are working on with the child and be asked to co-operate . . . or at least not undermine you. Good friends and family members who spend time with the child also need to work with you on the targeted behaviours. Work with helping professionals such as teachers to develop plans that are mutually supportive.

Here are some examples of situations where consistency is important for children and parents:

- Each time six-year-old Rob hit someone, he was placed on his 'time out towel', which went with him everywhere. It was not always easy nor convenient to put him in time out, but over time Rob learned that the time out towel was always the consequence for misbehaviour. It took a couple of months of consistently sitting in time out while his friends were playing before Rob was able to stop most of his hitting.
- Nine-year-old Kate is told that she cannot watch television until her homework is finished. In order to be effective, this rule must consistently be followed each school day. Some days it may mean that she and her friends need to do homework together before they can watch TV. When Kate is being watched by Grandma after school, Grandma checks to make sure that homework is done before the TV is turned on.

Sometimes it may be appropriate to act one way in one place or time but not in another. For example, it's okay to scream and yell at the basketball game in the school gym but it's not okay to scream and yell at the orchestra concert in the school gym. It's okay to jump on the indoor trampoline, but not on the sofa. If Mum likes flowers, why does she get upset when a child brings her roses from the neighbour's prize rosebush? These types of behaviours seem inconsistent to many children, and are often troublesome for substance exposed kids.

Predictability goes right along with consistency: can children depend on us to act the same way and provide the same supports? Children exposed to prenatal substance abuse can have problems with logical sequential thinking. "If . . . then . . ." is difficult for them to think through. This means that they need predictability in the adults around them. The adults can help children slowly develop this logical thinking when they react in a predictable manner to behaviours.

Whether the child's problems are organically related or emotionally related they often have significant difficulties with abstract reasoning, sequencing, and consequences. They need to have lots of modelling of "if . . . then . . ." actions, as well as direct teaching. Predictability and consistency in our actions and environment are important ways we help them learn this.

Persistence is an extremely important characteristic for parents to develop. It is necessary when dealing with all children, but especially children who have been exposed genetically or emotionally to parental substance abuse, who need to have many, many opportunities for success. Children are also very persistent when attempting to get what they want. Therefore, you must be persistent with them in getting what *you* want. You have to be as persistent as your child, if not more so.

Once you have decided on a behaviour in a child that you want to change, don't give up easily. You may have to change tactics to achieve success, but don't change too quickly or too often without giving your strategies a chance to work. You may learn how to shift direction from what doesn't work. You may have to take longer to achieve results than you wanted. If both of you are continually frustrated, it's probably time to either develop a new technique or set aside the task for a while.

When you target a behaviour for change, the behaviour may actually increase as the child attempts to "try you out" and see if you are serious. Although a younger child may respond to effective consequences for an uncomplicated task within a few days, more complicated tasks, particularly for substance exposed children, may take longer for appropriate responses. If after a couple of days or weeks you are seeing no change in behaviour, depending on the developmental level of the child and difficulty of the task, you may need to try something else. If it is working, be positive yet matter of fact about the achievement. If everything is praised as special, then nothing is really special. Provide opportunities to use new behaviours, both to practise and to reinforce.

Consequences

It is important that children learn that their actions have natural and logical consequences. Most children can learn this in their daily activities without too much difficulty when given the opportunity. Other children, who don't think logically or sequentially, need lots of extra help learning that consequences follow all actions. They have difficulty with the "if . . . then . . ." line of thinking. Parents help most children learn that all actions have consequences by allowing them to repeatedly experience the consequence of their behaviour and discussing the consequences. They allow the children to make as many choices as are appropriate and insist that they stick to their decision. With children who have difficultly with these concepts, it takes more support, cues, and practice before these are internalised.

In addition to a consistent routine and environment, practise cause and effect thinking and consequencing with games that teach sequencing, and practising chores or activities that require using these. Role play or practising with dolls, stuffed animals, or toys can also give children practice. Repetition is one of the keys to helping children develop these skills.

Here are some important things to keep in mind:

- Warning: It is important to involve other adults in the child's life (teachers, day care workers, extended family members, neighbours) in this learning process. If they are not involved it is possible that you could be accused of being neglectful or an uncaring parent.
- Realise that a task may be beyond a child's ability level right now. You may need to find alternatives to the task or build in gradual steps to accomplish it.
- Be flexible. If something doesn't seem to be working, look at the situation to decide whether it's within the child's ability and needs a different technique, or needs to be shelved for a while.

Here are some examples of how consequences could be used to teach appropriate behaviour:

- Hugh is careless at the table and spills his milk. The consequence might be that Hugh cleans up the mess, and perhaps has no more drink. If this is a child who is unco-ordinated at many tasks, you might want to try doing this in steps or environmental modification. Using a tip-proof cup or a covered cup with built in straw, like those used for bike riding, might be a positive interim step while working on the behaviour.

- Homework is left on the kitchen table in the morning. The natural consequences are that if the child can't get it in on time, grades suffer. But if this doesn't matter to a child, consequences don't encourage a change in behaviour. An alternative consequence for this child might be that if the student doesn't remember homework, the parent can't trust the child to bring in notes for class trips or special events; these might not get in on time if parents have to bring them in themselves. Working with the teacher may result in other possibilities or cues, such as homework taped to the lunchbox at night for a child who truly has organic memory problems.

- You tell your daughter the weather will be turning much colder during the day, and recommend that she would be warmer in jeans or a sweater. But she insists on a skirt and short sleeved blouse. The natural consequence is that the child (unless she isn't sensitive to temperature) will be cold and uncomfortable as the day goes on. *(This is one where you will probably have to engage the teacher's co-operation if you don't want to risk being reported for neglect.)*

Each of these examples provides children with an opportunity to learn from their actions. If I jump in to "protect" the child by giving more drinks, running the homework to school, going to school with warmer clothes, or driving the child to school, the children miss valuable learning opportunities.

Some children may need more interim steps and longer times to accomplish some of these tasks. After a while you may be able to predict the areas where your child is likely to have difficulties and need extra supports. Some children with delayed development may not be able to grasp these concepts on their own; they may always need someone to tell them when to wear a coat, take a bath, when and what to eat. This is where realistic evaluation and acceptance of the child's limits are important.

Some children who seem as if they will never get it eventually do; it just may take much longer for them to learn from their actions. Parents may be able to realise that their child will need more practice learning from consequences because he or she needs more time to learn other skills.

Some behaviours are just too dangerous to allow the child to experience the consequences. Most children could learn that running into the street is dangerous when allowed to experience the consequence. But the price is too high. Behaviours like playing with matches and gasoline, driving while drinking, darting into the street, jumping from roofs, and playing with guns need to be controlled through other parenting techniques, supervision, and environmental modification.

Clear, concise communication

Parents need to let children know exactly what we expect of them. Children with various developmental needs may not understand subtlety of voices, facial expressions, or long involved sentences. Their idea of what is said to them is often very different from what the parents mean to say. For example, if you say "Be home in time for supper," one child may know that means be home by 5.30pm but another may come home when they are hungry, because that seems like time for supper to them. We may not see the child before 9pm or she may be back in the kitchen in 15 minutes, depending on what her stomach tells her. "Be home by 5.30pm" is much more specific for a child, but some children will still have trouble with that. Even with a watch, they may not remember to periodically check it. For some children an interim step might be an inexpensive watch with a beeping alarm.

It helps to keep messages clear and specific and keep rules very clearly stated and to a minimum. The most important rules are those that directly impact on the child's and family's health and safety. The children need to know exactly what is expected of them; they are not good at guessing or remembering complicated rules and regulations. For example, "No hitting allowed!" tells the child exactly what the rule is, while "Be nice to others!" is open for wide range of interpretation. In the same way "I like the way you are sitting so quietly," tells the child the exact behaviour you like, but "You sure are good," does not tell the child what behaviour you see and like (and want repeated).

Positive attitudes

Parents seem to get more mileage out of positives than negatives. Try to use language that tends to be positive rather than negative. For example, rather than telling the kids what *not* to do, explain what we *want* them to do instead. Also notice and comment on when they are behaving in the manner you want, with specific behaviours described.

Here are some examples of positive statements:

"Yes, you may go to the park as soon as your homework is done." This is more constructive than the alternative: "No, you may not go now. You haven't finished your homework."

"We put books back on the shelf after reading these." This is better than the typical response: "Don't leave those books there. Didn't I tell you that before!"

Planning

If we can set up goals and plan for them ahead of time, we can anticipate how we expect the children to react and how to respond. For example, if waiting is difficult for the child, we need to plan appropriate diversions for the doctor's waiting room.

It's always helpful to have a contingency or emergency plan just in case something goes awry. For example, if I promise a treat from the vending machine after a child's clinic visit, I might want to have a treat stashed and available in case the vending machine is broken or I'm running late.

We must also plan on things taking a little longer than usual so that we do not have to rush the child beyond their capacity. Enough time needs to be planned for both the activity and any transitions involved with that activity.

Structure

Children who have emotional or physical residue because of exposure to parental substance abuse often respond best to simple physical surroundings. Try to keep the environment simple, not too busy, rushed or over-stimulated. For some kids each activity, situation, or environment will require structuring. For others only certain times or activities will need to be structured. Certainly there are periodic overload times when everyone needs to de-stress and simplify with limited distractions.

Sometimes structure will be something as simple as changing the music playing in the car. Rock and roll or some types of jazz can stir kids up whereas classical music, easy listening or children's tapes can soothe and create a calmer atmosphere. Sometimes any music or background activity is too much.

Structure of daily routines and transitions are also important. I find that active times followed by quiet activity work well with most children, regardless of prenatal history. It is often helpful to use quiet times just before certain activities of the day such as meals and bedtime.

Children usually need to be able to make as many choices as possible for their age and development, but some children get overwhelmed with too many choices. The parents must be sure that the choices offered to children are acceptable to the parents, regardless of what the child wants to consider as a choice.

Here are some examples:

1. *Helpful response:* "Do you want milk or juice with your eggs this morning?"

Non-helpful response: "What do you want for breakfast?" (Unless you are a short order cook.)

2. *Helpful response:* "Do you want to do your homework before supper or after?"

Non-helpful response: "When do you want to do your homework?" (The choice may be never!)

Once a choice is made, for me it is important that the child is made to stick with it, at least for a period of time. If children are allowed to change their minds many times, they are not learning the consequences of decision making. Sometimes in our effort to provide the children with a "good time" during the initial visits and homecoming we go overboard. Trips to the zoo, theme parks, the movies, and shopping are all fun and important. But later parents do not understand why the kids think money grows on trees, or why we can't continually just have fun. (We taught them that during the 'honeymoon'.) Sometimes these activities are better saved for times after the adjustment period. Even though we may want to rush in to make up for a lack of positive past experiences, these activities may be more beneficial once a child has settled in and begun to adjust to the structure of this family.

There are certain portions of the day that are especially difficult for some kids: meal times, bedtimes, transitions, and chores are some of them. Some families have found that there are ways to approach these times that make them easier (not necessarily easy, just easier!). Here are some suggestions:

Mealtimes: Increased stimulation can make this seem like feeding time at the zoo.

Try: Turning off all extra noise (TV, radio, tapes, phone);

Fewer food choices and smaller servings are less likely to overwhelm;

Setting up regular routines and chores for mealtimes – use a written chore list.

Kitchen: Since the kitchen is one of the most often used (and therefore messy and noisy) areas of the house for all family members, find ways to make it less of a problem area.

Try: Encouraging the children to help themselves as much as possible by keeping appropriate items within their reach (like plastic cups in low cabinets);

Allowing the children to help as much as they are able during preparation and cleaning up;

Keeping counter tops clear of clutter and unnecessary items (this especially helps to avoid distractions during mealtimes).

Bedtimes: This is one situation where physical structure as well as transition time must be controlled for some kids.

Try: Keeping the room simple with few distractions – posters or cute decorations may be too stimulating;

Limiting the number of toys or activities available at any one time (rotate these items for the child);

Younger children sometimes need the bedroom cupboards or storage areas locked for safety, to eliminate clutter, or to keep the child from dragging out those items you don't want them to have;

Limiting the amount of loud noises in the house at bedtime, use soft soothing music;

Routines that promote the transition to bedtime, such as bath time, story time with a parent, and being allowed to read quietly in bed.

Chores: Chores present a time when the child can learn much about themselves and their importance to the family, opportunities for success on many different levels in many different areas which help increase their self-esteem and independence. They are sometimes also stressful, boring, and/or targets for oppositional behaviour.

Try: Chore lists or charts (then they can refer to the list instead of arguing with you);

Simple descriptions, with or without pictures, of steps for complicated chores, new tasks, or chores a child repeatedly has difficulty with;

Rotating chores weekly to give children a chance with easy and hard levels of effort or boredom.

Transitions: Times of transitions are difficult for both parent and child. The adult must decide how much advance notice is required – how much is too soon or not enough. These are decisions that can only be learned by trial and error, child by child. Transitions must be made as much a part of the routines as possible. Give enough notice to allow them to finish the game they are playing, the TV show they are watching, or to finish reading the page or chapter they are on.

Routines

A calm, routine, structured setting where expectations are clear can help children understand what to expect and what is expected of them. Unpredictable settings can more easily trigger behavioural problems. Providing continuity through rituals and routines can help the child gain some sense of mastery over the immediate environment.

If at all possible, we try to keep the routine the same for each day. Weekends can be difficult for school age children because the routine of the normal school day is missing. Holidays and school breaks can also pose problems but bearing this in mind, families can develop structure and routines that do allow for spontaneous activities.

Activities such as mealtime, bedtime, and waking up that occur at predictable times can provide the child with a sense of structure. In between these normal, everyday activities, families can also plan non-routine activities. It is sometimes helpful to do "dry runs" or to "walk through" changes in routine. I try to explain this within the context of a routine day and use visual cues. For example, I might list the steps for a young child, holding up my fingers to count these as I explain: "After breakfast we are driving to Aunt Linda's. First, we will swim and play with your cousins. Second, we are going to have a barbecue and eat lunch. Then after lunch we are going to watch a video together. We'll be back home before supper."

Rituals are also an important part of structuring. Even though special holidays are not routine, the kids can understand the sameness of rituals. For example, visiting grandma and grandpa on Easter and hiding eggs can help make their "year routine" flow smoothly. You may need to alter rituals in order to match your child's developmental abilities. You can also use the routines of the year to help the child understand that you plan for them to be a part of your family in the future. Begin planning the family vacations after Christmas or a special festival or celebration. Talk about what you will be doing as a family during the spring break. During the summer plan the return to school in the autumn. The cycle of the year gives the children a sense of stability; take advantage of it.

Acceptance

All children need to be accepted as the person they are. Children who have been challenged by prenatal or early childhood parental substance exposure need this even more so. So many times they have been told, shown, or made to feel as if they are not important or don't count. They need to feel important and accepted just as they are. Only after they feel safe and secure in their acceptance can they begin to change. Often children have difficulty making changes an adult wants until they are sure that they are accepted as they are – even before they make that change. Once they are accepted they may be more willing to work to make the changes that please the important adults in their lives.

Parents must also be able to accept the fact that their child may not be able to achieve as much as they had hoped. Acceptance of limited success is often difficult for a parent who believed love was all the child needed, or given enough encouragement they could accomplish more. But it is very important to a child that parents can accept the child's limits while celebrating the abilities. Otherwise, children may end up feeling as if they disappointed their parents, that they are failures.

When you decide to work on changes, efforts at changing a child's behaviour should be limited to just one or two behaviours at a time. Prioritise the behaviours that must be changed and tackle the most important or the most accessible. Attempting to change everything about the child is overwhelming, both to the child and parent. Children also begin to feel that they must become someone else in order for the adult to love and accept them. I like the following quote from the book *Parenting Teens with Love and Logic* by Kline and Fay that describes that: "I don't become what you think I can and I don't become what I think I can. I become what I think you think I can."[1]

I feel it is very important to acknowledge the small victories that children have accomplished and the difficulties they may have encountered in achieving them. I also acknowledge their effort for trying even if the child was not successful. Children who have been prenatally exposed to drugs and alcohol can learn to find relationships with adults rewarding if acknowledgment of their efforts occurs. Also acknowledge the child's feelings so that the children recognise that their feelings are valid and real.

Some examples of helpful responses in this area:

- "You were able to keep your hands to yourself for a whole hour. That must have been hard for you. You must feel good about keeping your hands to yourself!"
- "The teacher said you hit Josh only once today! I'm sorry you're still having a problem but I bet that tomorrow you won't hit him at all!"
- "I know you worked very hard on your science project. You must be very disappointed that the teacher did not grade your effort."

Reinforcements

Most children learn that a job well done will give them a "self-satisfied" feeling. They are able to accept this feeling as the reward for doing something the best they can. Often children who have been prenatally exposed to drugs or alcohol cannot internalise these feelings. They need to have the reinforcements and rewards come from the adults in their lives for a longer period of time than other children. Recognition can be as simple as a pat on the back and being told "I see that you are trying hard to understand these maths problems." It may take longer for these feelings to be internalised so that the child can say to themselves, "I am trying hard to do this work."

Children with multiple needs (attachment problems, other emotional problems, learning difficulty or disability, and/or behaviour difficulties) may sabotage rewards. They may do this deliberately or unconsciously. You have to keep the child's needs in mind while planning what reinforcements and rewards are going to be used. Children with significant emotional needs may not respond to typical rewards or typical behaviour modification efforts. Remember, one child may be on different levels of development for cognitive, emotional, behavioural, spiritual and educational skills, and often these are not the same as their chronological age.

Some children will be motivated by the prospect of concrete rewards, like getting stickers for good behaviour. Other children will not be impressed by these but will gladly change their behaviour for the privilege of going to the shopping centre or cinema or having a friend over. For still other children it is harder to work out what would be appropriate. The child's efforts must be recognised quickly for the reward to be effective. Children are not able to delay gratification. Therefore, rewards should be given soon after the child accomplishes their goal. As the child becomes proficient the reward can come later.

Rewards may grow routine. The child may lose interest or change interests. What works for one child may not work on their sibling or neighbour. What interests the child today may not interest them tomorrow. Rewards work best when used to modify one behaviour at a time (two at the very most). Some examples:

- Mandy, aged nine, is told that she will earn the privilege of going skating when she does her chores without having to be repeatedly reminded. Each day that she completes her chores as agreed she gets a star on the calender. At the end of the week if she has five stars she is allowed to go skating. After a month, if she has succeeded each week she may take a friend along.

- Six-year-old Rob is told that he may ride his bicycle when he gets a good note from his teacher – no hitting classmates during the day. Bad notes – hitting his classmates – means he cannot ride that day. A few days after this was put into practice, he did not care whether he could ride or not; he had lost interest in the bicycle, but wanted gum after school. His mother decided that having gum required good notes from the teacher. Again, after a few days this was no longer prized. He then wanted to watch cartoons in the afternoon. So, once again his mother changed the reward for good notes to watching TV.

Positive experiences need to be provided to the children regardless of their behaviour on occasion. This tells them that they are special just as they are. Fun activities that the entire family can enjoy or the purchase of an item the child needs and wants can tell the child that no matter how they act, they are important and that they matter to you. This can be done occasionally just to catch them off guard. (It's fun to watch the expression on their faces when they receive something they feel they didn't deserve!)

Teaching new skills

Most parents don't spend a lot of time thinking about teaching children simple daily life skills. They assume children will learn them when they are ready. But children faced with the challenge of prenatal substance exposure often find learning these skills difficult. This can be especially true if the child also faces physical disabilities such as cerebral palsy.

Breaking the tasks into small steps ensures quicker success. A child can master one small process easier with less frustration. Some parents and professionals find children have the fastest success when a task is taught from finish to beginning, top to bottom, and left to right. Here is an example. You put the shirt over the child's head and pull down over the arms. The child then assists in pulling it down over the body. Soon the child is pulling it down over the body by herself. Then you show her how to put her arms in after you have pulled the shirt over her head. After she has mastered this step, you proceed to teach her how to pull the shirt down once it is on her head. The last step is to teach her how to put the shirt over her head correctly. This process helps children feel successful because they are finishing the task by themselves. They have a sense of mastery and reward for completion.

For very young children skills like feeding can be taught with the same technique of last to first: after you put food on the spoon and guide it into the child's mouth you allow the child to remove the spoon from the mouth. The next step the child learns is to guide the spoon, with your assistance, to his or her mouth. Lastly, the child learns to scoop the food on to the spoon.

For older children, tasks like household chores can also be taught with this same process. For example, making the bed can be broken into many small steps. After you have straightened the sheets and spread, and fluffed the pillows and are ready, allow the child to help pull the spread over the pillows. Once the child can pull the spread over the pillows, allow them to assist with fluffing the pillows and placing them on the bed and then pulling the spread over them. Next allow the child to work with you in straightening out the sheets and spread.

Working in these ways allows children to see concrete results of their efforts. They are then encouraged to continue working on the remaining necessary steps.

Other methods of teaching everyday skills include allowing the child to watch as you do the jobs, modelling the steps as described before. Also describe what you are doing as you work. You can also have the child show you how they think it should be done. Some skills such as using the telephone can be practised using play equipment and then moving to allowing the child to place calls to someone that you have arranged to help with teaching this skill. These methods can be combined so that the child is getting a complete picture of the importance of learning these skills.

Encouraging potential
All children need help developing to their fullest potential; children with special needs usually need more help. Adult expectations are part of that help, since children often will live up to or down to the adult's expectations. Here are some of the general principles I use in thinking about how to best help a child reach potential.

- Acceptance of the child is very important. When children feel secure, they want to work harder for the people that they know love and accept them just as they are.

- Appropriate expectations for the child are necessary to ensure good self-esteem. Make sure expectations are not so low that there is no challenge to the child, or so high the child is discouraged and, rather than have another failure, just doesn't try.
- Offer encouragement for their efforts as well as success.
- Acknowledge the difficulty of the task. Children often believe that everything is easy to others. They don't see or recognise the hard work others must put into success. So, it's important that we recognise that we know they are working hard to accomplish their goals.
- Recognise that not all children are college bound. It is necessary to plan their education to meet their interests, abilities, and potential. Help them find something they enjoy doing and do well.
- Give the child real life experiences. Don't protect them at all times from the consequences of their choices and actions unless physically dangerous.
- If certain skills are being worked on at school, try to incorporate them into daily life at home.

Basic real life skills

Because schools focus on academics and the interim steps to gain skills for academic achievements, practical issues that prepare children for the real world around them are not always included in the curriculum. There just isn't time for everything parents, or teachers, feel is important. Real life skills are important. These are basic, whatever the child's level of academic skill or ultimate goals. Some of these you teach at home, but they could also be reinforced at school. If your child has an Individualised Educational plan (IEP)* or statement of needs developed for him or her, when you work with the school look at ways these basic skills could be taught or reinforced within the framework or time limits of that plan. Be creative. Here are just a few of the basics to think about:

- Making change – how much money it takes to purchase items

---

*An IEP in the USA is a plan developed for each child in need of special assistance, services, etc, by school staff familiar with the child. It spells out specific goals and objectives and, once approved by school authorities and the child's family, is implemented.

- Reading a menu (even if it is a picture menu)
- Sorting cutlery and use of basic kitchen utensils
- Washing, sorting, and putting away laundry
- Simple cooking skills with stove and microwave
- Picking up after themselves
- Personal care skills such as dressing and washing
- How to locate help and ask for assistance
- Finding their way around their neighbourhood
- Meanings of basic street signs
- Basic medical information, for routine and emergency situations
- How to use, and not misuse, helpful tools like chequebooks, credit cards and bank cards, telephone calling cards, payment plans, etc.
- Safety skills
- Basic courtesy
- Work skills like effort, punctuality, etc

There are a number of things parents can do to help their children learn the needed skills for making it in the "real world". Although IEPs often seem to have no relationship to "real world" needs, some of the basic skills taught within that plan can be adapted. If your child is learning some of these basic skills, whether a preschool or high school student, you can help them translate these into practical skills by shifting tasks as in these examples:

- move from sorting pegs by colour, to sorting by shape, then move to sorting by items ie., shirts, socks, pants, knives, cups, etc.
- Start folding paper then move to folding fabric squares or napkins, then various items of linen and clothing.
- Move from rote counting to the simple counting skills needed in everyday life, like simple purchases by using a pretend shop. Later, help them at a real shop.
- Work on identifying items through the use of pictures, with the goal of identifying common signs (toilet, stop, danger) and order from a menu.
- Move from lacing cards and beads to lacing shoes (Velcro is a welcome interim step). Once simple lacing is mastered, try simple sewing, buttons, mending, or fun projects like sewing together a printed pattern

and stuffing it to make a toy.

- Playdough skills can be transferred to simple cooking projects like baking scones; microwave cooking can safely expand a child's repertoire.
- If children can learn how to use toys, they can learn how to appropriately use household equipment such as the washing machine, dryer, telephone, vacuum, radio.

Some children do best learning complex or multi-step tasks if they have one on one attention from an adult, with chances to actually do and practise the task. Some children also learn well when working as a group or team with an adult. This demonstrates the validity of the work: "If it is important enough that an adult will do it, then it must be important for me to learn it." Working with an adult also allows a natural setting for modelling the desired behaviour. Household chores lend themselves to working with an adult to learn self-sufficiency skills.

Even a child who cannot walk or has poor co-ordination can help put away selected groceries; toilet tissue and bars of soap can be dropped without too much damage. Older children can put away tinned goods or perishables, encouraging sorting and reading skills. Being put in charge of one set of items each time can give a child a sense of responsibility, capability, and pride. It can also help parents find out who didn't do their job correctly.

Children can enjoy helping in the kitchen during meal preparation. Young ones can stir or retrieve items from cabinets or the pantry. They can wipe down counters as you finish items. Meal time allows many opportunities to work with an adult for many skills. Even preschoolers can assist with setting the table, washing non-breakable dishes, putting away the cutlery and plastic items. Allow the child to help as much as developmentally appropriate and safe. Older children can prepare sandwiches, heat soup, scramble eggs and other simple cooking skills. Some children will be able to prepare complete meals even before they reach their teens.

Most importantly, children can be taught to be polite and can be fun to be around even if they can't yet spell, do division, or read Shakespeare, and even if they may never be able to accomplish this. We all know of bright, talented children who are obnoxious or lazy, and children who don't seem to be as gifted who go far on hard work, persistence, and a positive attitude.

We want our children to reach realistic goals, to be successful in managing within their environment as independently as possible. We also want them to have learned from our example a positive attitude about life. We hope that the structure, security and love of our family will be able to provide the safety to learn new things and eventually go into the world on their own with confidence. With this foundation, we encourage confidence that their family supports them, and the confidence that they are capable individuals.

References

1 Kline F J, and Fay Jim, *Parenting with Love and Logic*, Colorado Springs, Nav Press, 1990, USA.

5 Some suggestions and tools for planning

When we can plan ahead we are more likely to have at hand resources and alternatives to deal with the unexpected. Parenting children with special needs not only involves time and energy, it involves coping with unpredictable factors. Many families develop plans for the daily realities of family life to keep these at a more predictable pace, and post these where everyone has ready access to them: daily and weekly lists of chores; directions written down for specific steps to handle certain events, like using the blender, what to do in case of fire, babysitter instructions; an outline of daily routines for the family and/or specific family members; a weekly calendar of events, or a monthly calendar of events; and so on.

Some families also find it helpful to develop written plans for working on specific behaviours and needs. These don't have to be as elaborate as a statements of needs or a therapeutic treatment plan (although some parents do find more detailed planning useful). Sometimes just listing what has to be done, and then putting these in order of priority can help you put things into perspective. It can also ease the feeling that things are rapidly getting out of control because there is just too much to do. Sometimes it helps to write down next to each item when you will start (and perhaps hope to finish) each task. You could also jot down what you will need to get the job done. If you are really organised, you could also write down the steps needed to accomplish this. If you have done all that, then you have actually developed a plan after all!

Most parents give priority to the most urgent needs and then move on to long-term goals. Some parents decide to tackle the most "do-able" items first, and build up a sense of forward momentum. Still other parents insist that they just have to find out how to handle one particular behaviour or situation because it's so annoying it's driving them crazy. The way in which to structure your plan depends on your own style, and your experiences on which ways work best for you. You may approach things one way for some tasks or times, another a different time.

Worksheet 1

A family action plan (an example for you to think about)

Action plan for: Bill and Mary Jones and new son Tommy

Priorities	Strategies: Action, rules	Resources/Supports
Immediate	*Immediate*	*Immediate*
1. Tommy's bedwetting	1. drybed reward; medication; no bedtime liquids	1. ask grandma; call paediatrician
2. Tommy's nightmares	2. nightlight; his Teddy; therapy?	2. check with social worker and parent group
3. Mary's lack of sleep	3. take turns with Tom; catnaps at work? baby sitter.	3. check with neighbours – Buddy Family re sitters
4. keeping Tommy out of Bill's things	4. clear rules; wardrobe door lock; "Dad Time" for Tommy	4. lock at hardware store, extra key!
Long term	*Long term*	*Long term*
1. Tommy's fear of men	1. therapy; slow and easy steps with Dad	1. parent group meeting; social worker
2. keeping marital relationship strong	2. regular time away each week; taking time to share, other	2. take out old memories; talk with other parents; sitters
3. Tommy's learning issues	3. work closely with school; testing	3. parent group; school; reading
4. Tommy's hyperactivity	4. medication? coping tools?	4. parent group; doctor; reading; respite

Note: The above is taken from *The Parent Workbook* by Joan McNamara

Writing down a plan, simple or detailed, is helpful to clarify what needs to be done. Worksheet 1 is an example of one plan parents could use or look at to think about how their own plan should work. Worksheet 2 can be used by families for their own planning.

Worksheet 2
Family action plan

Action plan for:

Priorities	Strategies: Action, rules	Resources/Supports
Immediate	*Immediate*	*Immediate*
1	1	1
2	2	2
3	3	3
4	4	4
Long term	*Long term*	*Long term*
1	1	1
2	2	2
3	3	3
4	4	4

6   Considering placement

*A **home needed for Natalie***

Natalie is a neo-nate with unambiguous sexuality. She has sporadic emesis, minimal oropharyngeal secretions, and perianal lesions.

Natalie is enuretic and encopretic on a regular basis. She received prophylactic care for conjunctivitis neotatonum. Her strabismus is self-correcting.

The immature haemangioma present will require surgical repair. Her birth mother was a primigravida who experienced hyperemesis gravidanum and physiologic amenorrhea.

The agency with custodial responsibility and custody of Natalie is looking for loving parents with completed psychosocial placement summaries willing to give consistent care throughout her childhood and be fully committed to her needs. Are you that family?

More information about Natalie is available at the end of this chapter.

Considering placement

When a family is considering the placement of a child possibly exposed to parental substance abuse a lot of factors come into play, and a lot of information is needed, both factual and related to emotional issues. Some of this the social worker will have primary responsibility for, other parts the family will have to seek on their own.

The adoption or foster care worker presents a number of facts and pieces of information to the family in the beginning. It is ironic that foster families, who often have the hard job of helping children still struggling with recent loss or trauma, and most likely to consider adopting the child if he or she is free later (foster carers adopt the majority of special needs children in care in the USA), traditionally often get the least access to such information.

The social worker should have certain information available for the family when the child is first presented to the family for consideration. The family needs and deserves complete information in order to make an informed decision, but many times this is not available to the agency, or reports are written using jargon that is difficult to understand unless you are a professional, and even then can be inaccessible. Many times this means the worker has to work out what these reports mean in plain English (sometimes including his or her own reports) and be able to translate these for the family, including not just the facts but what these facts might mean to the child and new family. This also means the worker has to put in a lot of effort to locate as much information as possible from a variety of sources, some outside the agency. The following suggestions are at the same time both ideal situations and minimal guidelines for information to be included for sharing with the family:

1. Photographs of the child from as early as possible, and photos of the birth family and other carers and important people. Try to include the extended birth family, the hospital where the child was born, schools and daycare centres attended, former foster carers. These are helpful now, and invaluable later on for the child.

2. Social history of the child and family: Include any and all involvement with Social Services Departments and other services, history of abuse and/or neglect, drug use by family members, education and job histories, personal interests and talents. Foster care placements need to be included in this information. The length of time in each placement, age at time of placement, and reason for moves are all important pieces of information for the family to know. A brief school history should be included in this section, with more information available closer to actual placement.

3. Complete medical histories, when available, of both parents and any siblings; if at all possible, history of grand parents and extended family. The child's birth records, prenatal care records, and complete childhood medical records should be reviewed with the family, and also looked at by whichever medical professionals the family will be using.

4. Current school reports should include evaluations and the results, with interpretations of the results. Current placements should be

addressed. Reports from teachers, principals, and others dealing with the child.

5. Psychological or psychiatric testing, with interpretations; medications suggested, which ones used and what the responses are. Reports from psychologists and other therapists for review with the therapist that the family will be using.

Questions for the social worker

After the family has heard and seen all the information the social worker has presented concerning the child, there are some questions that still may need to be asked. The following are examples of some of the questions the social worker might be able to answer or help look for answers:

- When can I speak with the current foster carers? Can I talk with other previous carers?
- How long have you know this child? How long has this child been know to the agency?
- What differences do you see in the child now from when you first met?
- In your opinion, what do you think the range of potentials is for this child? Where do you see her five years from now? Or ten?
- What do you see life with this child to be like? (This is more likely to have a reality basis from foster carers)
- Who made the diagnosis? What evaluations were used to reach these conclusions?
- What do you see as his or her major area of need?
- With whom has this child made genuine attachments?
- Why is adoption by the foster carer not the plan?
- Will there be respite care available?
- What are the resources the child currently uses?
- What allowances are available for this child?
- What drugs did the birth parent use? To what extent and when during the pregnancy was the drug use?
- How much of the birth history does the child know?
- Has HIV testing been done for the birth parents and/or the child?
- Are there other families in our area that have adopted children with similar problems that we can talk to?

- Do you have the prenatal records, birth records, and paediatric records?

Questions for the foster carers

When you meet the foster carers they will hopefully be able to offer a wealth of information about this child based on their daily interactions. There may be some information they have that others do not, or that others forgot to mention.

- What is it like to live with this child on a daily basis?
- What is her daily routine?
- How does he fit into the family?
- What is the child's overall attitude? Is he basically happy, helpful, sad, lethargic, constantly on the go?
- Does she have friends in the neighbourhood and/or at school? How does she interact with them?
- How does she act with animals?
- Does he act his age? What age child is he more like?
- How much direct supervision is necessary?
- How long has the child been with your family? Are you interested in adopting him?
- What are her fears? How do you handle them? What comforts her?
- How does she act when stressed or tired? When angry?
- How does he respond to corrections and discipline? What works best? What doesn't work at all?
- How can her co-operation be encouraged at all?
- How can her co-operation be encouraged best?
- What are her behaviour problems? What seems to trigger them? Is there a pattern to her behaviours?
- What do you see in this child's future?
- What do you see as his area of greatest need? How do you think this can best be met?
- How is he doing in school? Is he appropriately placed?
- Can this child make real attachments? To whom is she attached?

Questions for the current school

As you are considering accepting a particular child into your family, there are many people to talk to that have a lot of vital information about the child. This may feel overwhelming at times. If the child is currently enrolled in a school, there is information available that you need access to in order to make an informed decision and plan effectively.

- How long has she been in the current placement?
- What progress has been made during this placement?
- Why is this considered appropriate?
- What other placements or interventions have been tried? What was it about them that didn't work?
- How does she interact with classmates?
- What evaluations were used to determine placement?
- What testing has been done – academic, psychological, IQ, etc? Who did it and when? What were the results?
- What do you see as his area of greatest need?
- What form of discipline works for him in the classroom?
- What does not seem to work?
- How does he act when frustrated?
- What areas are her strengths? How are these being encouraged?
- What subjects are most difficult for her?
- What classroom structure works best?
- How do I tell the school what we know? Who do we tell?
- Will they believe our suspicions, since it was not included in reports? How do I get it documented?
- Will the teacher know how to accommodate my child's needs? If not, how do I help?
- The school says since she is bright she shouldn't need anything special. She's doing okay now; should I push?
- How do I request special help, and what do I do if none is offered or available?

Questions for the doctor

As you move close to placement you will need to review the medical records available. When a child has specific medical needs sometimes you will be able to sit down with the doctor who provided primary care for the child to talk freely and candidly about the child's health and prognosis. If this is possible it can be helpful, since some information that otherwise is not available may be shared with you. Other times you may only have summaries of visits or the medical records themselves to tell you about the child. This is helpful but not as helpful as actually visiting the doctor. If you have access to the actual records, your GP may be able to review them with you. The questions that you will need answered may include:

- What is the prognosis?
- How was the diagnosis made? What tests were used? Who evaluated the results?
- What questions would you, as a doctor, like to have answered?
- How many times do you see these problems in your practice?
- What do you think life with this child will be like?
- What medications have been suggested? Which were used and which weren't? Why or why not? What were the reactions to or results of these? How long were they used for?
- Has the child had any operations, testing, or other medical procedures in the hospital?
- What other medical services does the child use?
- What do you see as her greatest need?
- Are his problems truly medical, emotional, or environmental? Permanent or correctable? What adaptations or compensations could be worked on?
- How soon can my paediatrician (or other specialists) receive copies of her records?
- Was post-natal drug testing done? Why? What were the results?
- What are the results of HIV testing? When was the last test performed? Which testing method was used?

Note: Obtain two copies of all medical records made available to you. One for yourself and one for your doctor. Ideally it would be helpful for these records to include prenatal history, birth records and the early paediatric records.

Questions for the therapist/counsellor

Many of the children who have been in foster care for any length of time or those children who were older when they came into foster care use counselling to help them deal with past and present issues. Counselling will usually need to continue once placement occurs. As you plan for the addition of this child into your family you will need to plan the continuation of therapy. To help with this transition here are some questions you may need to ask the current counsellor.

- Where did you see this child, emotionally and behaviourally, at the beginning of therapy? And now?
- How has the child responded to current therapy? What measurements are used to determine progress?
- How long have you been seeing this child?
- What do you see the future holding for this child? Where do you see this child in five years' time, and ten?
- What problems do you see that are not currently being addressed?
- What do you see as her greatest need?
- What parenting techniques need to be used with her?
- How long do you think he will need to be in therapy?
- Can you work with a new counsellor to ease the transition? Can you recommend someone in our area that is familiar with the problems and the methods you are using?
- What questions should be asked of new counsellors? How do we describe our child's needs to a new counsellor? What should we look for when we are considering a new counselling resource?

You will notice that the same questions or variations are asked of everyone involved with the child. Asking these questions of the different professionals will give you a composite picture of the child. You may get many perspectives, but when put together with other perspectives all the parts can give you a better glimpse of the real child.

Questions parents ask when considering placement

- We are considering the placement of an older child. The agency doesn't have a lot of history. What are the questions we should ask?
- The agency tells us the child we are considering was born into a family with a history of drug use, but not during pregnancy. Should we worry?
- What could show up later?
- Will he outgrow these problems?
- Are the problems currently experienced environmental, emotional, or organic? Are they part of delayed development?

- What resources are we going to need?
- What resources are now in use? Can we use these?
- What parents groups are available, how do we contact them?
- How much help can the agency offer us? What kinds of help? What post-placement services are most appropriate for our needs?
- Will the child be able to live independently as an adult?
- Is it ever too late to begin interventions?

Thinking about the many aspects of living with a particular child with special needs *before* placement helps you anticipate situations so that the routine isn't experienced as the unexpected, and the unexpected can be faced with a number of strategies. Often, families are so anxious to begin parenting that they do not consider some of the long-term implications of how this child may impact their family in months and years to come. Or they may be so anxious about potential problems they have a hard time seeing the child behind the labels. Talking with other experienced parents can really help you put abstract concepts into a reality based perspective.

We have included a worksheet on the following pages to help you think about some of the typical situations that come up in parenting a child who has been exposed to parental substance abuse. These are included for you to explore your comfort level in coping with them. Consider how you would feel helping your child with these issues and behaviours, and how you might feel in dealing with these situations in public. There are no right or wrong answers, only *your* answers.

Some dumb myths and other incorrect beliefs

Below are some 'answers' that we have heard that *do not* answer questions appropriately

- We can't change their history, why bother to tell anyone or even worry? Just accept the kids as they are!
- Since 'crack' is the worst drug known, the kids exposed to it are the most damaged.
- A few beers don't do any harm when you're pregnant.
- All they need is enough love.
- You can't make any difference, they're so messed up. Why bother?

- Most children affected by substance abuse are from minority ethnic communities.
- Most teachers don't need to know how to deal with these kids since they are all going to end up in special schools.
- They will outgrow it – it's just a phase.
- If you were a better parent, they wouldn't act that way.
- Dealing with "drug kids" takes much more training and resources (ie. costs too much) than our school has available.
- These kids are going to end up in prison because they are so aggressive; these kids are going to become addicts.
- These kids have no conscience.
- If he has so many problems why don't you give him back?
- What emotional problems in your life caused you to want one of these kids? (ie. What's wrong with you?)
- What emotional problems of yours caused this child to have such big problems? (ie. What's wrong with you?)
- Can't you make that child behave? (ditto!)
- He could if he really tried. She could if she wanted to.
- I'm a professional, I can handle it.
- These kids can't attach.
- The problems are all due to emotional issues. The problems are all due to organic issues.
- Just hang in there. If you are committed it will work.
- Just try harder.

Financial consequences

Children exposed to parental substance abuse may have special needs that are expensive to meet: daily medication; long-term counselling; tutoring; special equipment; appropriate child care and industrial strength babysitters; recreation and other programmes; more wear and tear. We do not like to think that our ability to parent a child is related to how we can meet the financial obligations to this child. But the added stress of trying to find and pay for needed services can be overwhelming at times.

Once again, planning before placement can help ease some of the stress. And again, talking with other parents may turn up special

Worksheet 1

Assessing comfort levels in parenting a child with special needs

If the child you wanted became a part of your family, how comfortable would you feel in dealing with the following, and with helping a child with the behaviours and issues expressed:

(Lowest comfort level = 1, highest comfort level = 5, uncertain = 0)

Situations your child presents	0	1	2	3	4	5
Child at age five wears nappies: at age seven still needs help with toileting						
Child may learn a behaviour or fact one day, not remember it the next, but be able to next week; uneven memory and performance						
Child can repeat directions or messages back but has difficulty sometimes connecting the information with what they are required to do about it; forgets part way through a task						
Child speaks like a much younger child; older child uses "babytalk" and/or mispronounces words; understands but has difficulty expressing what they want to communicate						
Compared to age level, child does not consistently follow rules, socially expected behaviours; conscience development poor						
Child very impulsive and distractible; easily overstimulated and/or stressed out						
Child looks "different" from other children						

Situations your child presents	0	1	2	3	4	5
Despite actual abilities, child does not perform well at school; is behind peers						
Child has trouble making/keeping same age friends; child socially inappropriate						
Child wets bed or has accidents during the day						
Child needs supervision due to inappropriate behaviour or lack of "common sense"						
Child does not respect personal boundaries of space, privacy, or property; child intrusive						
Child tells stories or lies, even about obvious or unimportant things						
Child has difficulty accepting touch						
Child has temper tantrums past preschool age						
Child will go with anyone, anywhere, anytime; no fear of strangers						

funding or financial plans, pitfalls of certain programmes, alternatives and discounts. Here are just a few examples of areas which may apply to your situation:

- If your child has unusual needs (or at least, unusual or infrequent for your area), are there providers in your area familiar with these and available to you? Are there people willing to learn about these?
- What are the financial resources available for your child's special needs in the community? Does your child qualify for them? Will he or she still be qualified after moving into your home? Would you and the child qualify for an adoption allowance?

- Have you discussed with your social worker the availability and provision of different services that your child may require?

All children bring certain expenses into the family budget: clothing, food, toys, and recreational expenses are necessary for all children. Children with special needs who may have extra needs to be met may bring extra expenses. Here are a few examples of the extra costs that some foster and adoptive families parenting children with special needs have suggested from their experiences. While many of these will not apply in your situation, they will give you an idea about "hidden" costs:

- Dietary needs: food allergies, high caloric needs that require expensive formulas, diabetic needs.
- Transportation costs for trips to counselling, doctors, recreation, education, etc. Multiply times number of children where appropriate.
- Much higher clothing and shoe use: braces wearing through clothing; dragging feet or crawling; very active children.
- Specialised equipment such as car seats, wheelchairs, braces, crutches, respirators.
- Appropriate child care and experienced babysitters may cost more. Multiply times number of children.
- Time away for parents: hopefully you can arrange respite care with other experienced parents for your children, but you may still need to spend money on food or lodging away from home.
- Extra child care costs for siblings while parents are involved in coping with one child's special needs.
- Lost wages due to time missed from work for necessary appointments or to spend with the child at home due to increased illness; school suspension days for bad behaviour.
- Extra expenses for child proofing the home: locks, window guards, outlet covers, gates, cabinet locks, etc.
- Structural changes needed to meet the child's needs – ramps, handrails, elevators, widened doorways; also, adjusting bedrooms or changing furniture.
- Replacement of belongings that are lost, stolen, lent or damaged by children.
- Tutoring.
- Specialised recreation programmes and camps.

Family strengths

In thinking about adding a new child to the family, it's helpful to look at what your family strengths and limits are. Where will you need help? How willing are you to ask for it? Questions like this are important as you think about parenting a child who may have special needs. The following worksheets are included to help you look at the strengths in your family. If you find that there are a number of areas where you don't seem to have everything in place, or will need a lot of resources, that doesn't mean you shouldn't think about adopting. What it does mean is that as you make an adoption plan for your family you may need extra time to look for resources to help you gain skills, learn more, and make some adaptations in your life. Especially in the area of special needs adoption, you may find that it is important to simplify a lot of things in your life before you complicate it with a child who comes into the family with many needs.

It is especially important to talk with other parents experienced in parenting children like the one(s) you hope to adopt. If you don't know any, ask your social worker. If you still can't seem to find a family whose situations are similar, check with PPIAS (Parent to Parent Information on Adoption Services), whose telephone number is listed at the end of this book. They may be able to help you get in contact with a family . . . and it may even turn out to be one close by!

Talk with other parents about the practical aspects of family living. What changed for them when they added this child to their family? What would they suggest about budgeting time, money, energy, in terms of family rules? What adaptations did they have to make emotionally, physically, financially? What suggestions would they have about arranging your home and adjusting your lifestyle? These are practical considerations that your social worker may know about but often hasn't experienced firsthand. Consumer tips from experienced families may save you emotional and financial resources.

It is helpful if you can work with someone on the following worksheets; if not your partner then a friend who knows your family and lifestyle. This is good practice for one of the most important rules in parenting a child with special needs: reach out to others for help and support. After you each fill out these worksheets about your family, compare them. Then discuss the issues and talk about how to encourage the strengths and provide effective supports for areas that aren't as strong.

Worksheet 2

Assessing family strengths

Looking at the following traits of healthy families, decide for each which rating you would give your own family.

Put "A" if you feel your family consistently puts this into action, "S" if you would rate your family as satisfactory, and "N" if you feel that this area needs improvement.

My family:

____ communicates and listens

____ affirms and supports; shows affection and caring openly

____ teaches and practises respect for others

____ works to develop trust

____ has a healthy sense of humour and play

____ shares leisure time; spends time together

____ shares responsibilities and has a balanced interaction

____ teaches and models right and wrong; uses logical consequences

____ has a strong sense of kinship and belonging, of "team spirit" and loyalty, with positive family traditions

____ has a shared moral and/or religious core; puts these beliefs into action

____ respects the privacy and personal boundaries of all of its members

____ values and puts into practice empathy and service to others

____ encourages family sharing at mealtimes, family meetings, other positive family patterns

____ has clearly defined roles, rules, and consistent discipline

____ acknowledges problems and seeks help and support

Note: Taken from *The Parent Workbook* by Joan McNamara

Worksheet 3

Family stress in parenting a child with special needs

This list has ten top stressors cited in family and parent surveys, plus contributions from foster and adoptive families. Rate your top stressor as 1 and least stressed area as 15. After comparing with your partner, discuss ways to reduce stress.

____ Family budget and finances

____ Children's behaviour/discipline/sibling conflicts

____ Not enough time as a couple/single parent nurturing

____ Unevenly shared responsibility in the family

____ Communication with children

____ Not enough personal time or privacy

____ Guilt and frustration: not able to do certain things or accomplish more

____ Couple relationship (communication/friendship/sex)

____ Not enough recreation/leisure time/family playtime

____ Overscheduled personal and family calendars

____ Insufficient information on children added to family

____ Sense of isolation; lack of understanding peers or support groups

____ lack of knowledgeable supports and services

____ Negative family and community responses because of child's needs and behaviour

____ Limited information and preparation on parenting children with special needs

Note: Taken from *The Parent Workbook* by Joan McNamara

Worksheet 4

Family strengths in special needs adoption

Look honestly at your family's strengths and limits for each of the following. After you rate your family, jot down what resources you could use to support and encourage these areas.

(Rating: Limited strengths = 1; Consistently strong in this area = 5)

Parental strengths	1	2	3	4	5	*Comments*
Parents can accept the unknown						
Parents can prepare for and accept a child's needs and limits while working to help a child access resources and reach potential						
Parents can ask for help when, or before, problems start growing; can have several alternative resources						
Parents can model appropriate behaviours for children						
Parents provide clear expectations and predictability of routines and responses						
Parents have solid personal support system of friends, family, other parents, caring professionals: parents take regular time out to use this						
Parents have at least one significant other in their life (not necessarily a love interest, but someone they can count on in hard times)						
Parents can provide secure structure with clear, firm rules						

Parental strengths	1	2	3	4	5	*Comments*
Parents can recognise that the child's behaviours are not always a personal reflection on their parenting or love but a symptom of child's experiences and feelings						
Parents can help the child translate behaviours and feelings into acceptable outlets (like active sports for the hyper child, caring volunteer work for the affectionate child)						
Parents can "personalise" the child's behaviours and step back to respond to child's needs rather than react emotionally						
Parents can actively use supports such as therapy, adoptive parent support groups, respite care, etc.						
Parents can provide continuing acknowledgments of child's efforts and reinforce appropriately						
Parents have the time and energy to deal with complex problems of child exposed to parental substance abuse						
Parents are comfortable with setting firm limits and specific rules, which may be more restrictive than for other children this same age						
Parents use logical consequences and alternatives, not physical punishment, as primary discipline tool; can detach and step back and teach rather than punish						

Parental strengths	1	2	3	4	5	Comments
Parents are willing to talk openly about the child's history when appropriate						
In two parent families, parents share decision making and parenting responsibilities						
Parents discuss feelings, concerns, and differences						
Parent take time to nurture their relationships. Single parents especially need to access close relationships that are supportive						
Parents encourage and support (emotionally, financially, physically) personal interest outside the family that increase self-esteem and decrease stress						
Parents are secure enough to handle negative or uninformed reactions to their child, family, parenting style and to reach out for support to others who do realistically understand						
Parents share a belief system that includes optimism, positive values and commitment to working towards a better world; these may be spiritual or religious or part of belonging to a faith community						

Resources checklist

You may find that some supportive resources for parenting a child exposed to parental substance abuse will be used right from the start, even before your child arrives. It may not be until much later that others are needed. Resources for some needs may not be available to you; they are still ideals to work toward. You may find that alone or with other parents you develop or encourage some of the resources needed by children and families. The checklist that follows can help you list what you think you will need. This is not meant to be a complete list, by any means, just examples to get you thinking. Talk with other experienced parents to get their input. Adapt this list, change things, add to it.

Worksheet 5

Supportive resources	Need	Have
Community		
Church willing to learn about child's needs and support you in your efforts		
Neighbours willing to learn about your child's needs and open to differences		
Sports and recreation programme open to including your child and adapting as necessary (Volunteers carefully screened)		
Parent support groups: adoptive and foster family groups and other special issue organisations		
Child care/after-school care/summer camps/industrial strength babysitters		
Respite care		
Others		
Medical		
Doctor or medical facility with specific services for your child within reasonable distance.		
Local special services – financial programme; physical, speech or occupational therapists, etc.		

Supportive resources	Need	Have
Doctor locally to co-ordinate local and extended services and address routine childhood needs		
Others		
Educational		
Flexible school administration at the school level and system wide		
Local services for special needs on site or close to home: speech therapy, smaller classes for children with special needs eg. learning disabilities, behaviour problems, etc., resource room, tutors, mentoring, counselling, and so on.		
Home or hospital based services if child has special medical needs		
Co-operative attitude working with other community agencies, including medical providers, on meeting child's needs: parents are partners in the team effort		
Child-focused and family-friendly		
Others		

Educational needs of a child with special needs or considered at risk for special needs must be met by the local education authority, but how the authorities or individual schools interpret and choose to respond varies greatly. A few authorities work co-operatively with other agencies to start services at birth; at the other end of the spectrum, parents tell of situations where staff unofficially encourage special education students to drop out of school.

Questions parents may have about their child's needs
- Will my child ever be "normal"? What is normal for our child?
- How can we tell when she's reached her maximum potential?
- When is it realistic to adjust our expectations?

- If he has learning problems, shouldn't we go easy on him?
- If she has severe learning disabilities, why expect her to learn some of these things, why bother to try?
- How can I find out what the problems really are?
- Does the child need to know why he, and people around him, are having so much trouble?
- Is my child at risk for drug or alcohol use later?
- Do you think there is a higher risk that my child was sexually abused? Or that she'll be abusive?
- Will there be other problems later? Is my child at higher risk for learning difficulties?
- How do I tell my child about his history regarding the birth mother's drug use? How much do I tell?
- Who do I share this information with about my child's special needs? Is it better not to tell some people? How do I talk to my mother about this?
- How do I explain all of these issues to my child?

Questions related to parent and family needs
- Why didn't the birth mother tell us that she had used drugs/alcohol during her pregnancy?
- Shouldn't the agency help us find help, even though the adoption has been final for several years?
- Why didn't the agency tell us he would have these problems?
- Do we tell the other kids why she has some problems?
- What do we tell my mother?
- How will this child in our family impact on the others?
- He seems so smart . . . Why does he keep doing stupid things?
- I treat all my kids the same way. Why does this one not respond like the others?
- Will our family ever be the same? Will we get back to normal?
- What kind of help will our family need in the future?

A note about HIV issues
When thinking about the adoption of a child who has been affected by parental drug use, the reality of HIV infection must be considered. Children born to a mother who is HIV positive will be born testing

antibody positive. This does not mean that the child is actually infected with the virus. It does mean that the child is carrying the mother's antibodies to the virus. Most of the children born HIV positive will not be infected; their HIV antibody test will become negative somewhere between the ages of 10 to 18 months. Only between 15–20 per cent of these children are actually infected and will go on to become sick. There are new better tests available to diagnose HIV infection; by 3–6 months of age, it is generally possible to know if a child has HIV infection or not.

As medical care improves and knowledge of HIV/AIDS grows, the life expectancy of children infected with HIV lengthens. In the mid 1980s a child with HIV was not expected to live to see his or her first birthday. In the late 1980s, medical authorities in the USA felt that children born with HIV would not live long enough to enter school. Now, the best estimate is that children who are HIV infected can live up to 9–12 years of age. What will happen as the children grow, whether better care and more research will continue to mean longer lifespans, is still an unknown.

The preparation for parenting a child who has HIV infection must be based on the reality of daily living with the child's multiple needs – emotional, physical, educational, spiritual – not just on the medical issues of HIV or on preparing the family to deal with grief. Children who have HIV are often exposed prenatally to multiple substance abuse, with the multiple needs that go along with that label. Charts at the front of this book outline some of those possibilities. All of the child's history and needs must be addressed. The homestudy for a family willing to parent a child who has HIV should focus on living with the child, not on helping the child to die.

Living with a child with a chronic or terminal condition is often not easy. Neither is living with uncertainties. Problems like mental retardation, cerebral palsy, language delays, and emotional disturbances are all possibilities, as well as recurrent ear or chest infections and poor eating. However, some children may remain very well for a number of years. Children may need many resources to assist them with meeting the challenge of developing to the fullest. Because the problems and potential problems associated with HIV/AIDS seem so overwhelming, we can lose sight of the child and only see special needs, labels, and difficulties.

The resources currently available to you and your child in the community will need to be explored. Here are just a few of the issues to think about:

- What is ready for you to tap into? What resources are you going to need to develop? Do you have the time and energy to develop them?
- How will the local churches, medical community, or your social circles react to this child joining your family?
- What are the current attitudes in your extended family or community concerning HIV and related issues? Can you live with these attitudes or are you going to have to work on educating and changing attitudes?
- How open are you going to be concerning the child's diagnosis? How are you going to decide who you share the information with? When do you share?
- What are the resources the child is currently using? What will they need in the future?
- If an infant is HIV antibody positive, and not sick, there is a chance that the baby is not infected with the virus. Can you live with the child and all of the problems and unknowns if it turns out that the child may have a normal life expectancy?
- Can you live with being put on a pedestal as a saint for adopting "the poor dying orphan"? Or being shunned as somewhat "unbalanced" for taking on this child, and for "endangering" others?
- Are you willing to continually educate yourself about the latest medical advances? Are you willing to consider experimental treatments?
- Do you have support services available to assist your family when the child begins to develop problems? Can you ask for help when the going gets rough?
- If there are other children in your family, are they able to accept and adapt to the multiple needs of the sick child? How will you help them deal with a sibling's possible death? What resources can you access for their emotional needs? What about yours?

Feelings while parenting a drug exposed/HIV positive child: personal reflections on the hard issues

Liz Grimes

Guilt and resentment: This may sound like a strange combination of emotions. However, this is how it became so mixed up for me: I chose to accept this child and the problems that are part and parcel of him. Then I wondered why I did it, and if I want to continue parenting this child. Then I feel guilty for having these feelings. Sometimes I resent the time and energy required by this child. It seems as if all I do is give without getting anything in return. Then you feel guilty for feeling the resentment.

Scared: I feel scared of loving this child to only have him die. I feel scared at times of opening my family to public scrutiny if we are open with the diagnosis. Scared of not loving the kid enough. Scared of loving him too much. Scared that you wanted and worked for something that may be more than you can handle.

Envy: I feel envious of normal families. But I also feel envious of families with children more severely disabled than mine. They don't disrupt everyone around them.

Embarrassed: I am embarrassed by the way I must deal with my child in public – the use of gloves, administering medicine, methods of behaviour management, the use of special equipment. Also I feel embarrassed by the way my child behaves in public.

Tired: I become tired of being a martyr and educator. I get tired of sleepless nights, tired of fighting for services my kid needs and deserves. I get tired of being tired!!

Remember the adoption listing about NATALIE you saw at the beginning of this section on Placement? Here is a translation of that write-up into plain English.

A *home needed for Natalie*

Natalie is a newborn girl. She spits up a little, has normal mucus secretions, and a slight nappy rash. Natalie has normal bladder and bowel control for an infant. She received routine eye drops to prevent syphilis of the eyes. Her crossed eyes should straighten as she grows. The strawberry birthmark can be easily corrected. This is her birth mother's first pregnancy. She had morning sickness and no bleeding.

The agency is looking for a family willing to love and parent this beautiful child.

This is an example of how the use of jargon can cause confusion, and make prospective adoptive parents turn the page to another listing that doesn't sound so scary. You don't even get the chance to recognise the children who might fit well into your family. When you see language as complicated and specialised as in the first writeup on Natalie, be sure that you ask the professionals to interpret what sounds like secret code into everyday language. Then visit experienced adoptive families and foster carers in your area. Talk with them about what this might mean within your family.

7 In conversation with children

With thanks to Amanda, Katherine, and Zachary Grimes (and parents Liz and Jac Grimes)

With such a great deal of information in the media and at schools about the effects of drugs and alcohol, children exposed to parental substance abuse can begin to think about their own history, yet sometimes not be able to express their concerns and questions. Certain information or misinformed classmates may add to the confusion. It is important that adults in their lives encourage sharing, giving them opportunities to ask questions and voice their concerns in a supportive environment.

In answering questions, keep in mind the child's developmental level, and understand what it is the child really wants: the specific type of correct information; personal history; reassurance; how this all relates personally today. Don't give too much information and overwhelm the child; don't give so little that the child thinks you don't know or don't want to talk about their concerns. Provide truthful answers at the emotional or developmental levels appropriate to your child; provide a truthful base for future questions.

You will need to think about answers that:

- are truthful, but geared to the child's level of understanding – when you don't know, say so;
- will provide an appropriate basis for more complex information or discussion you may share at a later time in the child's development;
- are expressed in language that you are comfortable with and children can understand;
- are simple, short, and to the point;
- express your own disappointment when information is missing or not available – offer to look for it;
- demonstrate respect for the child's ability to process through difficult or confused feelings, to own negative as well as positive feelings, and to change their mind;
- do not "sugar coat" or romanticise or paint an all negative picture of the facts.

Some examples of sharing with children are presented by the answers that follow from one adoptive/foster mother, Liz Grimes, to her children. Remember that this is how *one* mother felt comfortable sharing information with her children; answers are detailed since her children were older. Her children's situations and needs may be different from yours. Take into account your child's developmental level, ability to process information, current emotional needs and ability to handle difficult information, and ability to focus attention, particularly when handling difficult issues. You may have a different style or approach, and that's okay too.

Answering some questions

● *Why did she use drugs?*

Your birth mother had an addiction to drugs. An addiction is so strong a need for drugs or alcohol that the person can't seem to stop by themselves. They need help to stop.

● *Couldn't she find another way to work out her problems?*

Often, someone using drugs does not realise that there are other ways to solve problems. Sometimes the person may not realise that it is a problem.

● *Did she solve her problems?*

We don't know for certain if she did work out her problems. Sometimes as people grow older they learn new ways to solve problems. Maybe she has worked on some of them. What are some problems you think she might have? How do you think that she could solve them?

● *Didn't she care more about me than she did about drugs? If she loved me why did she keep on using drugs?*

When people have an addiction, they cannot choose to use or not to use. Their bodies must have the drugs. It is not really a matter of love or care. The drugs are more powerful and stronger. Only when someone gets special help can they overcome their addiction. It's a little bit like when you have a bad cough: you don't want to cough, you don't like to cough, but you can't help it. No matter how much I love you or you love me, that bad cough won't go away until you get special help for it – medicine. An addiction is sort of like that – the person needs special help to stop taking drugs.

● *If she stops taking drugs, can she take me back?*

(Answers will be different for foster and adopted children. For foster

children, court, agency, or birth family plans will affect these answers.
Talk with children about their concerns and, if appropriate, their own
wishes for the future.)

For an adopted child: Adoption is for always. Once you are adopted your
birth parents cannot come back to get you. You are with this family now
and this is your forever family.

For a foster child: The judge and social worker have said that when your
birthmum has finished treatment and has got a job, they will see if she
is ready to take you home and take good care of you. What do you think
your birthmum will say to them? What do you think they will say? Is
there anything you want them to know? What do you hope she will say
and they will say?

- *My birthmum is still using drugs. Can I run away and be adopted?*
  (question from a foster child)

Sometimes children are old enough to know that living with a parent who
uses drugs (or alcohol) is not safe. You may think that nobody can help
you. But running away just makes more problems: where would a child
your age sleep? How would you get money to eat? Who would protect
you? The smart way is to talk to adults you trust to find other ways to
work on this big problem.

- *Can my adoptive mum start using drugs and give me back to my birth*
  mum?

Sometimes adoptive parents have problems and need help to work these
out, but usually they know how to work on their problems without using
drugs or alcohol. Adoption is forever, your adoptive parents cannot give
you back to your birth parent.

- *Did my birth dad do it too?*

(If it's not on record:) We don't know. Since your birth mother did,
chances are he also did. What do you think?

- *Did she die from using drugs?*

We have not heard from the agency about your birth parents in a long
time. We know that when you were five years old they were still alive.
If the agency had heard about your birth parents' death, I think they
would have told us. So I think they probably must still be alive.

Note: Special care must be take in answering this question if the birth
parents have died. Work with professionals on helping the children with

this. There may be work that children will need to do to explore and express their feelings; often children will have misinformation and a sense of guilt; they may feel relieved or have mixed feelings.

● *Could her brain be messed up because of drugs?*

Using drugs can damage a person's brain, sometimes a little, sometimes a lot. Unfortunately, one of the reasons your mum couldn't take care of you or be your forever mum is because she damaged her brain so much with drugs. She couldn't take care of herself, so she couldn't take care of a child either.

● *Does my birth father know that I am OK?*

(One answer:) Unfortunately, your birth mum chose not to tell your birth father that she was pregnant with you, or did not know or say who he was. So he does not know that you were born and are growing so well. It is sad that he misses out on knowing you.

(Another answer:) Your birth dad knows the agency took care of you and found a safe place for you to grow up. Maybe he thinks about you sometimes.

● *Could I have problems because my birth mum drank and/or used drugs? What kind of problems?*

(This is a long discussion. Often you will give brief information and find you return to the issues again as your child has new questions or is at a new developmental stage.)

Sometimes babies do have problems if their birth mums use drugs or drink during the pregnancy. There are lots of problems that babies can have, some are serious and some aren't so serious. Babies can have big problems like severe learning disability, or cerebral palsy; they can be very tiny when they are born, cry a lot, have trouble eating or be sick a lot. As they grow up they may have trouble learning new things, have trouble paying attention in school, have trouble learning to walk or talk, or be really active; sometimes it is hard for them to make friends. Other babies are born with no problems or they do not have problems that last into their school years. Some babies are born with problems that are not very serious. Do you think that you have any problems because your birth mother used alcohol? What problems do you think you have or are worried about?

● *Why couldn't my birth father keep me?*

Your birth father also had an addiction and could not take care of you the way that you needed and deserved to be taken care of. So, with the help of social workers and the judge, it was decided that a new family, that could take care of you, would be found and you would be adopted.

- *Will I use drugs when I grow up? My birth parents did.*

I hope that you won't use drugs when you grow up. Just because your birth parents used alcohol or drugs doesn't mean you have to. Some people have strong reaction to alcohol so it is easier to become addicted; this reaction can run in families like allergies or having brown eyes. But even if your family had this allergy does not mean you have to drink. Now that you know about it you can make better decisions about drinking. The choice is yours.

- *Do I have other brothers and sisters in my birth family? Do they have the same problems as me? Did they keep them? Did they keep them because they didn't have any problems?*

Note: This question can be answered factually, but one of the underlying questions is "Was I given away because there is something wrong with me?" There is almost a catch-22 problem here: if other children without problems were kept in the extended family (or previous foster family) it infers something wrong with this child; if other children with problems were kept, why didn't they keep this child? If the child did have a problem that birth parents cited as a reason for difficulties it makes it harder for adults to assure children that the adults had the problem in this situation, not the children.

- *Why can't we help her stop drinking?*

Since I don't know your birth mum or know where she lives, I can't help her. Besides, that's not my job. One person can't make another person stop if they don't want to. My job is that you are taken care of and loved and that you get all the help that you need. Other people have tried to help your birth mum. I don't know how to take care of people with drug and alcohol problems, but I do know how to take care of you.

- *Can the birth parents make their children take drugs?*

While the baby is growing inside the mother, all of its food comes from the mother through a special cord. If the mum takes vitamins, some of the vitamins go through the cord to the baby. If the mum takes medicine some of it goes through the cord into the baby. If the mum drinks alcohol or takes drugs, some of the alcohol or drugs go into the baby through the cord. So, in one way parents can make their children take drugs. Most parents that use drugs or alcohol don't want to have their kids using them.

● *Can't a person get AIDS from drugs? Did my birth mum?*

(This question requires preparation and careful thought before answering. If you don't have answers, get assistance.)

Yes, using drugs is one of the ways a person can get the HIV infection. We do not know if your birth parents are infected with HIV. You came to us at a time when the agency did not know a lot about drug use and HIV. Would you like us to check with the agency to see if they know?

(Note: If you have been notified of the birth parents' HIV status, you will want to talk with a counsellor on how to best answer this question. Truth concerning this is best, but lots of education must also be done. Contact your social worker, local AIDS advice organisation, or health worker for additional help. You may also want to consider the need for testing of the child you are parenting.)

8 Adopting a drug-exposed infant
Current information to make your decision easier

Dr. Jerri Ann Jenista MD

Adapted with permission of the author and "OURS Magazine", Adoptive Families of America.

Are you thinking about adopting a drug-exposed baby? Are you worried and confused by the conflicting stories you see in the media? Are you looking for the right answers about cocaine, drugs, babies, and adoption?

Then read no further. This story is not for you since no one really knows what's going on. But read on to find out what we do know so far.

You don't have to use a lot imagination to realise that drug use and adoption are intertwined in our society. Drug use is one of the many factors resulting in a child's need for adoptive placement.

Even the most flawed and controversial studies of drug exposure during pregnancy indicate that the problem is far more widespread than we can imagine, affecting even the most isolated areas of our country. Therefore, before you adopt, you should consider the potential for exposure to HIV, alcohol, drugs, abuse, or neglect.

A lot of information

Vast amounts of literature exist on the effects of alcohol, cigarette smoking, and other drugs such as heroin or marijuana on the newborn infant. You can obtain reasonable facts on these problems from many available sources. Information about cocaine and crack, however, isn't as clear.

Three or four years ago, every second news story seemed to describe the devastating effect of cocaine on the unborn child. We read about a generation of children doomed to social and educational failure. It seemed that no intervention was successful with these children. And the number of cocaine exposed babies was a tidal wave poised to overwhelm already inadequate educational and social resources. No one but a saint would adopt such a child.

Meanwhile, of course, there were families who had unknowingly already adopted infants affected by prenatal drug exposure. Slowly we began to hear stories from them. Some of these stories were horrifying, but many had reasonable outcomes.

At the same time, the medical literature began to shift. In the past year or so, we've begun to see scientific articles and editorials describing cocaine-exposed infants who are functioning far better than previously expected. Researchers have begun to tell us about children who cannot be distinguished in any reliable way from their non-exposed peers.

Confusing information

As adoptive parents, who and what are we to believe? The problem with every study published on cocaine and babies is in the interpretation. As you learn to be a critical reader, you'll discover some major difficulties with *all* drug studies.

First, we have no reliable means of determining drug exposure. There is no interview technique, laboratory test or feature of physical examination that can divide all new babies into an "exposed" or "not-exposed" category.

In one study of more than 1,000 mothers, had the researchers accepted only what the mother had said, 24 per cent of drug-exposed babies would have been missed. A urine test of the baby on the day of birth would have missed 47 per cent of the exposed infants. Even if we were able to test every mother every day during pregnancy, drug tests of urine would detect only the drugs for which we were looking. If we do not know to look for a new or different drug, we will not find it.

In the reading of any study comparing exposed and non-exposed children, you must ask yourself, "Can I be absolutely sure that no drug-exposed children were accidentally included in the drug-free group?" The result of such misclassification is to make drug-exposed children look better than they really are.

The next difficulty in evaluating any drug study is in determining causation. The researcher accepts only babies whom he or she is sure were cocaine-exposed. Can the researcher be equally sure that any abnormalities found in those babies were caused by cocaine? How can the researcher be sure that the mother didn't use other drugs, alcohol, or cigarettes? Perhaps the effects the researcher sees are not due to cocaine but to the other things that often go along with cocaine use such as inadequate diet, family violence, poor medical care, or sexually-transmitted infection. Maybe it is not the drug at all but the environment where the drug is used that is causing bad effects. Because it is so difficult to determine that cocaine by itself caused the effects we see, researchers tend to hesitate in their conclusions. Instead they say, "The bad effects we saw were *associated with but perhaps not caused by cocaine*".

As adoptive parents, it is important for us to search for those words carefully. If cocaine does not cause the bad effects by itself, perhaps the child can be helped by changing the environment. That is, if cocaine is associated with but does not actually produce the problems, perhaps the child will do better when removed to an adoptive home without all those drug-related problems. This is actually an area of vigorous research right now, but we don't know the answers yet.

The third problem with drug studies is in determining the outcome. When the researcher decides to see if prenatal cocaine exposure has any effect on babies, he or she has to choose what to use as an outcome measure. The researcher needs to decide which bad effect to study.

In adults, cocaine affects mood and behaviour. So, it seemed sensible to look at those things in babies too. Unfortunately, we don't have a good reliable test to determine whether an infant has a normal "mood". Instead, we take a leap and say, "If babies do not have normal moods and behaviour, they probably won't develop normally. If they are having problems controlling how they feel and think, they probably won't have time to do the normal baby things they are supposed to be doing." So we use developmental or neurological tests on these children. We then compare the results to those of children from the same background who were not cocaine-exposed. And when such studies have been done well, cocaine-exposed toddlers have been found to be not different from their non-exposed neighbours.

As a prospective adoptive parent this sounds helpful to me. And, as a matter of fact, it is these studies that we now are reading about in the popular literature in the USA. It looks as if there is some hope; something in the brains of these babies does work right.

But do these tests tell us what we want to know? The families who are having problems with their drug-exposed infants do not complain that the children have severe learning disabilities. What bothers them is the child's behaviour. Short attention span, poor judgement, rapid and wide swings, and impulsivity disrupt family life.

We don't have good tests to measure these sorts of characteristics. But if these are the true effects of cocaine exposure, what will happen to these children as they grow older? You can be a hyperactive impulsive two-year-old without too much damage to your life. But, if you still act that way in primary school, are you going to be able to keep up with your classmates when they learn the multiplication tables?

Long-term outcomes

A major area of worry (and study) is in the long-term outcome of drug-exposed infants. The oldest group of carefully followed babies (in the USA) are now only in the early years of primary school. No one can know what will happen to these children as adolescents or adults because none of the children are that old yet. Likewise, although Foetal Alcohol Syndrome was first reported in the USA in the 1970s the first adult outcome study was not published until 1991 because we had to wait for the first group of children to grow up. If someone tells you that he or she can predict how your cocaine-exposed newborn is going to grow up, don't believe it. No one knows.

Another difficulty with drug studies is the reporting of results. Many studies are done that never reach the medical literature. As a matter of fact, in a review of materials presented at paediatric research meetings in the USA, only 11 per cent of studies showing no effect of cocaine were discussed but 57 per cent of those showing a deleterious effect were presented! Thus, we are never really sure that we are getting *all* the information. Perhaps there are more important data out there. The topic of cocaine and babies is new in science, however, and it will take years for all the facts to surface.

A final problem with drug studies is that none of them addresses what adoptive families really want to know. Let's suppose that maternal cocaine use does result in some effect on the newborn child, whether or not we can detect that effect early on. If we place that child in an adoptive home, away from all association with drug use and if we subject that child to early intervention through the schools and with knowledgeable therapists, can we reverse, erase, or ameliorate the effect of the drug? At this point, we simply do not know. Only few adopted children are included in most studies of drug-exposed babies. And the final results of those studies are not available.

What we know

There are a few things we do know about cocaine-exposed babies. Drugs are not good for any baby. No matter where you stand in the drug controversy, we all agree that it would be better never to have been exposed.

Some data give a fairly reliable picture of drug-exposed infants. Many of these babies are premature and/or small for their age. They may have a smaller-than-expected head size. Some, but not all, babies have a drug withdrawal syndrome that may last for weeks or months consisting of abnormal sleep patterns, poor feeding, jitteriness, or irritability. Many infants are hard to console; they avoid interaction with their carers. A few babies are at risk of major defects such as stroke, seizures or other brain abnormalities, or defects in the retina of the eye. Several studies indicate that these babies are at slightly higher risk of Sudden Infant Death Syndrome.

What are the percentages attached to each of these problems? No one is quite sure. Some defects may be clinically silent; that is, they never cause harm to the person and would never be discovered except for a research study. Others, such as massive stroke in the brain, are dramatic and are probably recognised quite quickly. Many other problems initially reported to be caused by or associated with prenatal cocaine exposure have not been proved in subsequent studies.

At present, the best we can say is that there is a small group of babies with severe problems that can be detected fairly early, within a few months of birth. There is another larger group of infants who suffer behaviour problems due to drug withdrawal. These children may be extremely difficult to care for in early infancy. Finally, there is a large unknown group of children who may have suffered subtle brain damage leading to behavioural changes. We do not yet know how widespread those effects are and whether or not they can be lessened by early intervention.

What you can do

If you are considering adopting or already have adopted a drug-exposed child, collect as much information as you can. Attend any useful conferences, read relevant literature, and talk to foster carers and adoptive parents who are already doing this.

Evaluate critically every piece of information you get. Does this new finding apply to your child under his or her circumstance? Do not expect your paediatrician, education authority, or social worker to know all the answers. Unless those professionals have a lot of experience with drug-exposed infants, you are probably going to know more than they do.

Make sure you have a strong support network in place before the child enters your home. Will your local authority provide respite services, allowances for medical expenses and therapies, post-adoption counselling or support groups? Do you have friends or relatives who can relieve you if this child is more than you expected? Are there parent groups nearby or accessible by phone to provide help in a crisis, guide you to helpful professionals, or advocate for you in the schools?

Children who come into adoption because of drug use in their environment may not be typical of all drug-exposed babies. They may be the "bottom of the barrel." But they may have the best hope for the future. If you are considering adopting a baby exposed before birth to any drug, be prepared for the worst, but expect the best. As one expert from Yale University commented, "Crack kids are not broken".

9 Under the influence: alcoholism and the adopted child

Katherine M Davis MSW

Reprinted with permission from the author and "OURS Magazine", Adoptive Families of America.

Are you aware that alcoholism in the biological family puts your child at risk – even if placed for adoption as an infant? Recent medical research recognises alcoholism as a disease with specific signs and symptoms. Like diabetes or high blood pressure, alcoholism runs in families. Children of alcoholics run a high risk of becoming alcoholics – even if they've never lived with alcoholic parents. Sons of alcoholic fathers, for example, are four times more likely to become alcoholics, even if adopted as infants. A child with one alcoholic parent runs a 52 per cent chance of developing alcoholism; a child with two, a 90 per cent chance.

What can we as parents do? Are we helpless in the face of a child's genetic history? "The potter who works with clay recognises the limitations of his material," writes Margaret Mead. "He must temper it with a given amount of sand, glaze it thus, keep it at such and such a temperature, fire it at such a heat. But by recognising the limitations of his material, he does not limit the beauty of the shape that his artist's hand, grown wise in a tradition, informed by his own special vision of the world, can impose upon that clay."

Helping our children

Parents need to know about alcoholism and provide their children with appropriate information according to age level. For instance, a parent might say to a young child, "Some people get sick when they eat sugar; their bodies are made that way. Beer and wine can do that to you."

Older children need to know that the negative effects of alcohol for them won't necessarily be immediate, but can build over time with serious long-term consequences. In fact, children who exhibit organic vulnerability to substance addiction typically exhibit fewer symptoms than their peers when they abuse alcohol. For example, they may exhibit behaviours such as fewer intense feelings of intoxication and less motor impairment than their peers who consume comparable amounts of alcohol.

Peer support groups may be able to offer positive alternatives to societal pressure to try alcohol. Peers supporting peers can be an extremely powerful positive force in the lives of teenagers.

Children who have lived in alcoholic families typically suffer an additional burden: they adapt to the chaos and instability of their environment by developing an extreme need to control ("I trust no one"), an excessive sense of responsibility ("It's my fault they drank"), and denial of feelings ("It doesn't hurt"). Children who have lived in alcoholic families often develop low self-esteem, insecurities, and a heightened need for attention, making them easy prey for victimisation. Substance abuse in a family also increases the risk that a child will be abused or neglected. All of these factors can contribute to emotional stress and emotional problems. Although there is controversy in this area, some feel that this may make it more likely that a child already genetically predisposed to alcoholism would begin to experiment with use of alcohol.

Many adult children of alcoholics who have chosen not to drink still live "under the influence," feeling depressed, isolated, and guilty. Self-help groups are springing up across the USA for adult children of alcoholics to learn to live with their histories and vulnerabilities by coming to trust their own feelings and perceptions and by learning to accept that a person doesn't have to be perfect to be worthy. In the USA, some schools and counselling services have started groups for children focused on helping children with emotional issues related to substance abuse in the family.

Here are some helpful suggestions for parents:

- Be a good role model. Your child picks up what you do, not what you say.
- Know the facts about alcohol and alcoholism.
- Support your child. Be an advocate, not a judge.
- Be alert to unexplained changes in behaviour or personality.
- Seek professional help when there is a problem. Delay simply allows the problem to worsen.
- Be patient. Solutions take time. Relapses are to be expected.

Some of us learn earlier than others that we cannot protect our children.

Being the child of an alcoholic is an unfair burden – but so are many of the other ways these precious survivors have experienced pain, trauma, and loss. We can give ourselves and our children hope that as they come to know the nature of their clay and accept its limitations, they can, like the potter, create new patterns.

10 A Bill of Rights for parents of children with special needs

Adapted from an article by Joan McNamara in "OURS Magazine" and reprinted with permission of the author

As a parent of a child with special needs you have rights too. Make sure you enjoy these, because martyrs are seldom appreciated, especially by their children. You need to have your own "gas tank" full in order to be able to handle your family and their draining needs.

1. Get a life: enjoy life as intensely as you can; take up hobbies and interests outside the family.
2. Have hostile thoughts once in a while without feeling guilty. Take time to ventilate, to gripe, and complain to someone supportive.
3. Enjoy being alone by finding a time and place for privacy.
4. Have a vacation (however short) without children; a date with your partner; take weekends away; find time to nurture important relationships.
5. Let your children take responsibility for the consequences of their own actions, especially by giving them tasks within their ability and chances to succeed.
6. Don't feel obligated to always be cheerful or to always tell the truth about how life is going. Try "it's moving along," or "it's just about the same," or "I don't feel like talking about it."
7. Give strokes to adults and to children, and get them back in return. Look for people and places where you feel good.
8. Share positives about how others are doing, especially with your child. Give specific reinforcement, not global.
9. Act respectfully and demand respect. Tell others when you have a problem with what they are doing.
10. Spend a little extra money on yourself. Budget for small luxuries; budget for time spent on yourself and feeling good.
11. Congratulate yourself for being a good and capable person doing a difficult job.

11 Another Introduction

This book concerns children who often look at things differently than those around them. With or without being given labels to describe their special needs, they often need not just extra help but different approaches to help. To help *you* look at things differently we have included a second introduction at the back of the book, instead of the front. It is an introduction to three young people starting their adult lives with gusto and determination.

Sandy is one of those men who would rather be outside than inside, working than relaxing. He takes on life with high energy. At home he likes to tinker, which can be irritating to his wife when the baby is sleeping. At work he sticks to his schedule and puts in hard work, making him a valued employee. Sandy has worked in airport maintenance and recycling, and is taking courses to increase his skills in auto body work.

Wanda has a flair for colour and fabric. She only has to see an outfit once to be able to reproduce it for herself, friends, or family, often with more style than the original. Wanda worked for several years after high school, then decided she was ready for college. She researched different courses, got a grant, and was admitted to one of the colleges she had chosen. Working and going to college at the same time can be tough, but so is Wanda.

Kevin has not yet decided which course he will choose when he finishes school this spring. In the meantime, his last year is busy for him: he has excelled in two sports; wrestling and the rifle team; he competed (and won) in weightlifting on a state level; he is balancing a full academic load with sports and a social life. Kevin does all his classnotes and assignments on his computer.

Now let's backtrack, and look at reports about these young people before they moved into their permanent families. At that time, neither parents nor social workers knew much about exposure to parental substance abuse and the complex ways their effects can touch children's lives. All three were older children given multiple "special needs" labels, like "developmentally slow". In preschool pictures of Sandy it is possible that some of the features associated with prenatal alcohol are present. Substance abuse was possibly a contributor to the neglect that brought Wanda into care. Kevin's teenaged birth mother continued to use cocaine during the pregnancy, even after she almost died from an overdose.

At various points during their growing up years, labels were discarded and others were added. New diagnosis from new professionals replaced old ones. Therapy, medication, special classes, foster placements, parent support groups, recreation programmes, teenage therapy groups, and family counselling were some of the resources accessed to provide support for the children and their new families.

Parenting these children was not an easy or routine task. The labels, diagnosis, and resources parents found often didn't seem to fit the children or the families. Children sometimes carried labels into school settings designed for children with those labels, for example, yet still didn't seem to find what they needed there. It was often confusing for parents and for children. At times parents felt like only sheer stubbornness kept them going.

Often decisions were made to reject what one parent called "cookie cutter solutions" appropriate for most children and families, and strike out to invent new approaches that seemed to work better for their particular situations. Working harder was necessary, but only one part of the whole answer. Looking at things differently, and creatively, and sharing information with other parents with children like theirs seemed to work better. Nurturing a family life that was accepting, structured, and consistent was positive for the children, and encouraged sanity for everyone.

If current information about the effects of exposure to parental substance abuse had been available to these parents and to the professionals working with them, perhaps some of the symptoms and behaviours would have made more sense, and could have had more effective responses. Perhaps not. Even if this information had been in place, other issues, like separation and loss, multiple moves in care, unrelated medical problems, and the temperament of children and family members, would still have had to have been addressed. But an understanding of the issues of exposure to parental substance abuse may have provided a more relevant framework within which to develop more effective planning for their family. And it could have provided additional insights into the physical and emotional reasons why symptoms and behaviours existed and persisted.

No one has all the answers. No one has a crystal ball to look into the future. Life for someone affected by parental substance abuse can have sharper edges, deeper lows, heightened sensitivities. Often the expectations are that you should suppress the parts that don't match the general population, and reshape them to look the same as others. But that would be to lose the insights that could be gained from understanding experiences like sadness, to ignore the unique perceptions that can sometimes come when you don't see the world just like everyone else. After trying to get around Liverpool with a road map of Leeds, you may find you learn more interesting things about Liverpool than a lot of other people. Sometimes if you let go of the road map and look around, you can find that the view is interesting despite the bumps, or even because of them.

It is hard work. And yet looking at the lives of the three young people profiled here, we can see that they have built successful, positive lives even though they may not have travelled on the same paths as others. Many of the same symptoms and problems that contributed to earlier labels are still issues, but these labels don't define them, don't seem as important within the whole picture of the richness of their adult lives.

Each of these three have also touched the lives of others in positive ways, breaking earlier cycles of abuse and addiction. They are starting a new generation of children affected by parental substance abuse, a generation of hope.

Glossary

Abruptio placentio: The early separation of the placenta during pregnancy or delivery.

Abruptio placentae: The early separation of the placenta.

Addiction: The psychological and/or physiological dependence on a substance or habit.

Anoxia: A condition that occurs when the oxygen level of the blood has become lowered to the point that brain injury can occur.

Bonding: The ability between a child and primary carer to make a deep, affectionate connection.

Camptodactyly: The abnormal curvature of the fingers.

Cardiac arrhythmias: An irregular heart rhythm.

Central nervous system (CNS): The brain, spinal cord, and nerves.

Cerebral infarction: The death of brain tissue resulting from an insufficient blood supply.

Cerebral palsy: A motor disability characterised by paralysis, poor balance, weakness, and poor speech.

Clinodactyly: The abnormal curvature of the fingers; often seen in FAS patients.

COA: Children of Alcoholics, a term coined to describe adults who grew up in alcoholic families and share some typical characteristics because of that emotional experience.

Confabulation: A behaviour where a person readily gives answers to questions without regard for what the actual truth or reality is. Rather than deliberate deception or lying, it seems to be a persons's attempt (often unconsciously) to fill in the gaps in knowledge or memory with plausible information. Someone with uneven memory might use this, especially when stressed, in order to be co-operative or helpful.

Crack: The street name of freebase cocaine manufactured into crystals or "rocks" which cracks when heated; considered to be more powerful than powdered cocaine.

Dysfunction: Term that refers to not functioning, or working, appropriately or fully; can refer to medical issues or psychological issues, such as a "dysfunctional family".

Dyslexia: A learning disorder which can cause problems with reading and writing. Although the exact cause of the disorder is not clear, some experts attribute the problem to genetic links and chemical imbalance.

Dysmorphologist: A physician who specialises in birth defects.

Epicanthral folds: The folds at the inner corner of the eyes, often seen in FAS.

Failure to thrive: A medical condition in which an infant or child is failing to develop mentally and physically.

Foetal Alcohol Effect (FAE): Condition that occurs when a woman abuses alcohol during pregnancy, usually resulting in central nervous system dysfunction and growth deficit. It is the cluster of prenatal alcohol abuse effects with fewer symptoms (especially physical), making it harder to diagnose, *not* a milder form of FAS.

Foetal Alcohol Syndrome (FAS): It occurs when a woman abuses alcohol during pregnancy. The diagnosis of FAS includes three categories: growth deficiency for height and weight; distinct facial features and physical abnormalities; central nervous system dysfunction, including learning difficulties.

Foetal haemolytic disease: The breaking down of red blood cells.

Genitourinary: The genitals and urinary organs.

Growth retardation: A much slower rate of growth than normal, especially in height and weight; also called growth deficiency.

Hemangiomas: A benign lesion caused by dilated blood vessels.

Hypertonic: Stiff joints or muscles, very common in babies prenatally exposed to cocaine.

Hyperactivity: In children, hyperactivity is characterised by excessive activity, distractibility, and impulsiveness. It may increase, with a sense of loss of control, when a child is overstimulated or overstressed.

Hypersensitivity: This term is sometimes used to describe emotional oversensitivity or physical overresponsiveness to stimuli. Some people affected by prenatal substance abuse may be hypersensitive to bright lights, the texture of objects or food, touch, sound, smell, or sensory overload from environmental stimulation or stress.

Hyposensitivity: The term used to describe the reverse of hypersensitivity, where an individual does not seem to respond appropriately to pain, heat or cold, noise and other sensory experiences, or possibly, even pleasurable stimuli.

Impaired foetal oxygenation: A condition in which there is insufficient oxygen carried by the blood to the tissues.

Information Processing Deficit: A term used to describe difficulties or gaps a person may have related to areas such as translating information received from one sense – such as hearing – into appropriate action in another sense – such as writing or acting on directions; generalising information and using cause and effect reasoning; perceiving similarities and differences and understanding abstractions.

Microcephaly: A condition of small head circumference.

Micrognathia: The abnormal smallness of the jaw.

Neonatal: The first four weeks after birth.

Neonatologist: A physician who specialises in work with newborns.

Neurologist: A physician who specialises in diseases of the nervous system.

Nystagmum: A constant, involuntary movement of the eye; a characteristic of FAS.

Otitis media: An inflammation of the ear.

Palpebral fissures: The opening between the eyelids. Prenatal abuse of alcohol can result in shorter fissures for the affected baby, with small eyes relative to the space between the eyes.

Perseveration: Term which describes the action of engaging in the same behaviour over and over again; can be an indication of emotional or physical overload, or difficulty with making transitions.

Philtrum: The vertical grooved area between the lip and nose.

Prenatal: Period or during the period before birth, during pregnancy.

Ptosis: The drooping of the eye or eyelid, often seen in FAS.

Seizure: A condition caused by abnormal electric activity in the brain, may result in unconsciousness, and twitching or jerking of muscles.

Spina bifida: A defect in which the spinal column fails to close completely during foetal development. This condition can have mild to serious effects such as paralysis and/or loss of bowel and bladder movement.

Strabismus: An eye disorder in which both eyes cannot properly focus together, usually associated with lack of muscular co-ordination.

Syndrome: A term to describe a cluster or pattern of symptoms, signs, or characteristics which indicate a particular condition; can be a medical or a psychological term.

Tactile Defensive: A condition where a person is so overstimulated, usually by touch, that they avoid it. This can be misinterpreted as rejection or aggression. Some children still have an overwhelming need to touch, and can be inappropriate, intrusive, or overaggressive. Also called "kinesthetic hypersensitivity", it can also be sensitivity to light, sound, taste, smell.

Teratogen: A substance which can cause changes in normal foetal development and growth.

Teratogenic effects: The development of birth defects in the foetus, usually because of tertogens.

Further reading

Books for parents

Batty D (ed), *HIV Infection and Children in Need*, BAAF 1993.

Dorris M, *The Broken Cord*, Harper Perennial, 1989, New York, USA.
A father's true story of his adopted son with FAS, with detailed factual information from the early 1990s.

Fahlberg V I, *A Child's Journey through Placement*, BAAF 1994.
An essential reference and resource book which contains much practical guidance on working with children in the care system.

Kleinfeld J, and Westcott S, (eds), *Fantastic Antoine Succeeds*, University of Alaska Press, 1993, Fairbanks, USA.
An anthology of articles by parents and professionals on educating children with foetal alcohol syndrome.

McNamara J, *Resources for Families Adopting Sexually Abused Children*, Family Resources, 1992, Greensboro, USA.
Information and lists of resources.

McNamara J, and McNamara B H, *Adoption and the Sexually Abused Child*, University of Southern Maine, 1990, Portland, USA.
An anthology of helpful articles on wide-ranging issues of child sexual abuse and adoption.

McNamara J, *Tangled Feelings: Adoption and child sexual abuse*, Family Resources, 1988, Ossining, USA.
A short booklet for adoptive parents discussing issues of child sexual abuse affecting children and their new families.

McNamara B H, and McNamara J, *Parent Workbook: Adoption and the sexually abused child,* Family Resources, 1990, Greensboro, USA.
Contains readings, activities, worksheets, and resources on adoption and child sexual abuse issues.

Villarreal S, McKinney L, and Quakenbush M, *Handle with Care: Helping children prenatally exposed to drugs and alcohol*, ETR Associates, 1992, Santa Cruz, USA.
Contains information on FAS/FAE, drug abuse, prenatal issues, and educating young school children.

Sanford D, *Love Letters*, Multnomah Press, 1991, Portland, USA.
Letters and suggestions about helping hurt children.

Smith S, *No Easy Answers: The learning disabled child*, National Institute of Mental Health, 1978, Rockville, USA.

Books for children

Cunningham C, *All Kinds of Separation*, Kidsrights, 1988, Mount Dora, USA.
Deals with feelings that occur when children are separated from parents. Addresses divorce, physical and sexual abuse, and drug and alcohol abuse.

Garth M, *Moonbeam: A book of meditations for children*, Collins Dove Press, 1992, North Blackburn, Victoria, Australia.
Short images for children on calm and creativity.

Gehret J, *Eagle Eyes*, Images Press, 1991, Fariport, New York, USA.

Gehret J, *The Don't-give-up-kid*, Verbal Images Press, 1991, Fairport, New York, USA.
A children's story about learning difficulties.

Hausher R, *Children and the AIDS Virus*, Clarion Books, 1989, New York, USA.
A book for children, parents and teachers on the subject of AIDS.

Houlton B, *Tad and Me: How I found out about fetal alcohol syndrome*, Hazelton, 1991, Center City, Minnesota, USA.
A story told by a child whose friend has FAS, with information about both facts and feelings.

McNamara J, *SAFE Kids*, Family Resources, 1986, Ossining, New York, USA.
A simple book for children and grownups to share about personal safety.

McNamara J, and McNamara B, *The Ordinary Miracle*, Family Resources, 1980, Ossining, New York, USA.
Story to share about foster care, orphanages, sadness, adoption, and growing in love.

Rosenberg M B, *Not my Family: Sharing the truth about alcoholism*, Bradbury Press, 1988, New York, USA.
Children share about their experiences with an alcoholic parent.

Rosenberg M B, *Growing up Adopted*, Bradbury Press, 1989, New York, USA.
A collection of studies based on interviews with children of alcoholics.

Simon N, *Why am I Different?*, Albert Whitman & Company, 1979, USA.
An explanation of difference from a child's perspective.

Most of the above books published in the USA are available from:
Bookstall Services Ltd, 86 Abbey Street, Derby DE22 3SQ. Tel: 01332 368039 Fax: 01332 368079. It is possible that they may be able to obtain others for you.

British Agencies for Adoption & Fostering publishes several other titles on adoption, fostering and child care issues. Please send an sae (29p) for a free catalogue to BAAF, Skyline House, 200 Union Street, London SE1 0LY.

Useful resources

BAAF Head Office
Skyline House
200 Union Street
London SE1 0LY
Tel. 0171 593 2000

Parent to Parent Information on Adoption Services (PPIAS)
The Laurels
Lower Boddington, near Daventry
Northants NN11 6YA
Tel. 01327 260295

National Foster Care Association (NFCA)
5-7 Marshalsea Road
London SE1 1EP
Tel. 0171 828 6266

Post-Adoption Centres
Organisations that offer advice, counselling, information, training and self-help and support groups to adopted people, birth families and adoptive families.

Post-Adoption Centre
5 Torriano Mews, Torriano Avenue
London NW5 2RZ
Tel. 0171 284 0555

After Adoption
12-14 Chapel Street, Salford
Manchester M3 7NN
Tel. 0161 839 4930

After Adoption
Yorkshire and Humberside
82 Cardigan Road
Leeds LS6 3BT
Tel. 0113 2302100

West Midlands Post-Adoption Service
92 Newcombe Road, Handsworth
Birmingham B21 8DD
Tel. 0121 523 3343

Adoption Counselling Centre
Family Care
21 Castle Street
Edinburgh EH2 3DN
Tel. 0131 225 6441

Barnardo's Scottish Adoption Advice Centre
16 Sandyford Place
Glasgow G3 7N
Tel. 0141 339 0772

IN THE USA

Family Resources
1521 Foxhollow Road,
Greensboro, North Carolina 27410
USA
Tel. 0101 910 852 5257

For information about other publications and materials referred to in this book contact Family Resources at the above address.